OHM'S LAW, ELECTRICAL MATH and VOLTAGE DROP CALCULATIONS
By Tom Henry

While every precaution has been taken in the preparation of this course to ensure accuracy and reliability of the information, instructions, and directions, it is in no way to be construed as a guarantee. The author and publisher assumes no responsibility for errors or omissions. Neither is any liability assumed from the use of the information contained herein in case of misinterpretations, human error or typographical errors.

National Electrical Code® and NEC® are Registered Trademarks of the National Fire Protection Association, Inc., Quincy, MA.

 ENRY PUBLICATIONS SINCE 1985

Second printing February 2006   **ISBN 0 - 945495 - 26 - 9**

A German Georg Simon Ohm (1787-1854) developed Ohm's law.

Although he discovered one of the most fundamental laws of current electricity, he was virtually ignored for most of his life by scientists in his own country.

In 1827 Georg Simon Ohm discovered some laws relating to the strength of a current in a wire. Ohm found that electricity acts like *water* in a pipe. It is a simple law that states the relationship between voltage, current, and resistance in a mathematical equation.

Ohm discovered that the current in a circuit is directly proportional to the electric pressure and inversely to the resistance of the conductors.

Ohm's Law is one of the most important things that you will use throughout your electrical career. It is a mathematical tool which is of the greatest use in determining an *unknown* factor of voltage, current or resistance in an electrical circuit in which the other two factors are known.

This book was written as a study-aid for an electrician preparing to take an electrical examination. The electrician normally works on the left side of the decimal and the electronics person on the right side. In this book the electrician will learn the right side of the decimal point.

The intent of this book is to give the electrician a refresher on theory, Ohm's Law, explain AC and DC in layman terms, harmonics, give you easier to understand formulas, show sketches of circuits, explain the function of the neutral conductor, etc.

Included in the last section of the book are Voltage Drop Calculations.

As you read this study-aid book you will note that complicated electrical formulas and explanations have been put in a clear, concise understandable language for the *electrician*.

"Written for an electrician by an electrician".

TABLE OF CONTENTS

ELECTRICAL HISTORIANS

Did Edison invent the light bulb, Marconi the radio, Bell the telephone, Morse the telegraph? The answers are no. They didn't invent the wheel. They were instrumental in making it better and in some cases obtaining the patent.

Electrical history goes back before Christ and brings us to the computer age. Along this journey you will discover it took several people along the way to make the light bulb glow.

An American Benjamin Franklin (1706-1790) kite experiment demonstrated that lightning is electricity. He was the first to use the terms positive and negative charge.

Franklin was one of seventeen children. He quit school at age ten to become a printer. His life is the classic story of a self-made man achieving wealth and fame through determination and intelligence.

James Watt (1736-1819) born in Scotland. Although he conducted no electrical experiments he must not be overlooked. He was an instrument maker by trade and set up a repair shop in Glasgow in 1757.

Watt thought that the steam engine would replace animal power, where the number of horses replaced seemed an obvious way to measure the charge for performance. Interestly, Watt measured the rate of work exerted by a horse drawing rubbish up an old mine shaft and found it amounted to about 22,000 ft-lbs per minute. He added a margin of 50% arriving at 33,000 ft-lbs.

An Englishman Michael Faraday (1791-1867) made one of the most significant discoveries in the history of electricity: *Electromagnetic induction.*

His pioneering work dealt with how electric currents work. Many inventions would come from his experiments, but they would come fifty to one hundred years later.

Failures never discouraged Faraday. He would say, "the failures are just as important as the successes." He felt failures also teach.

James Maxwell (1831-1879) a Scottish mathematician translated Faraday's theories into mathematical expressions. Maxwell was one of the finest mathematicians in history.

A *maxwell* is the electromagnetic unit of magnetic flux, named in his honor.

Today he is widely regarded as secondary only to Isaac Newton and Albert Einstein in the world of science.

Thomas Alva Edison (1847-1931) was one of the most well known inventors of all time with 1093 patents. Self-educated, Edison was interested in chemistry and electronics.

During the whole of his life Edison received only three months of formal schooling, and was dismissed from school as being retarded, though in fact a childhood attack of scarlet fever had left him partially deaf.

Nikola Tesla was born of Serbian parents July 10, 1856 and died a broke and lonely man in New York City January 7, 1943. He envisioned a world without poles and power lines. Refered to as the greatest inventive genius of all time.

Tesla's system triumphed to make possible the first large-scale harnessing of Niagara Falls with the first hydroelectric plant in the United States in 1886.

October 1893 George Westinghouse (1846-1914)was awarded the contract to build the first generators at Niagara Falls.

Westinghouse invented the air brake system to stop trains, the first of more than one hundred patents he would receive in this area alone. He soon founded the Westinghouse Air Brake Company in 1869.

He used his money to buy up patents in the electric field. One of the inventions he bought was the *transformer* from William Stanley.

Otto Hahn (1879-1968) a German chemist and physicist made the vital discovery which led to the first nuclear reactor.

He uncovered the process of nuclear fission by which nuclei of atoms of heavy elements can break into smaller nuclei, in the process releasing large quantities of energy.

Hahn was awarded the Nobel prize for chemistry in 1944.

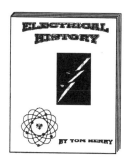

If you are interested in learning more about the history of electricity I invite you to read my book "Electrical History" which starts 500 years before Christ and brings you to the present day of lasers and fiber optics.

THE BEGINNING

What is electricity? It was discovered over 2000 years ago by the Greeks. They noticed that when they rubbed an amber material together with a cloth material, it became charged. The Greeks called the amber **elektron,** this is how the word electricity came to be.

The word telephone is derived from Greek words meaning "to speak at a distance". Many of the words used with electricity are from the Greek alphabet, such as poly, delta, omega, kilo, theta, etc.

What is electricity? This question is still unanswered. Defined as "that force which moves electrons". Today little more is known than the ancient Greeks knew about the fundamental nature of electricity, but enormous strides have been made in harnessing and using it.

Electrical energy can be generated, not **electricity**. Electricity can neither be created nor destroyed. All matter is composed of electricity. Matter is defined as anything that occupies space and has weight.

Electricity was **discovered**, not invented. The dictionary defines it as "one of the fundamental entities in nature".

During Benjamin Franklin's time, scientists thought electricity was like a fluid with positive and negative charges that flowed through a conductor.

Today it is generally agreed that electric current flow is comprised of moving electrons. This is called the **electron theory**. Electrons are very tiny particles of matter.

Electricity is **produced** when electrons are freed from their atoms. This can be done from six different ways.

MAGNETISM	- GENERATOR
CHEMICAL ACTION	- BATTERY
LIGHT	- PHOTOELECTRIC EFFECT
HEAT	- THERMOCOUPLE (dissimilar metals)
PRESSURE	- PIEZOELECTRICITY (crystals)
FRICTION	- STATIC ELECTRICITY

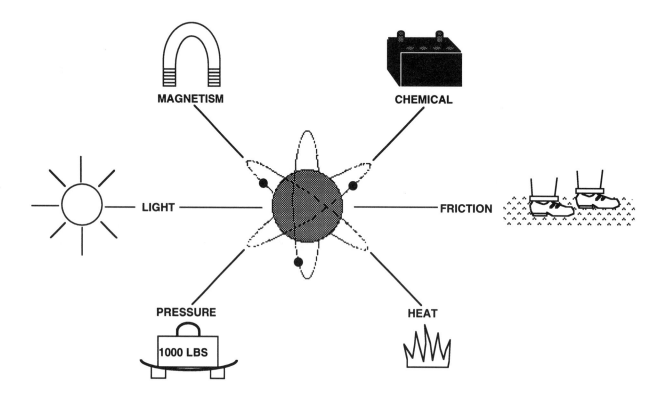

The number one producer of electrical energy is the generator which employs the principle of **electromagnetic** induction.

 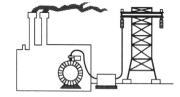

When atoms are added or taken away from the molecules of a substance, the chemical change will cause the substance to take on an electric charge. The process of producing electron flow by **chemical** action is used in **batteries.**

Voltage produced by **pressure** is referred to a **piezoelectricity**. Voltage is produced by compressing or decompressing crystals of certain substances. The power capacity of a crystal is very small. When a crystal of quartz is compressed into a different shape electrons tend to move through the crystal. The crystal is able to convert mechanical force, either pressure or tension, to electrical force. The fundamental reasons for this action are not known. However, the action is predictable, and therefore useful. Crystals are mainly used in communication equipment.

When a length of copper is **heated** at one end, electrons tend to move away from the hot end toward the cooler end. However in some metals, such as iron, the opposite action takes place and electrons tend to move toward the hot end. The heating of two dissimilar metals at a junction causes thermoelectric voltage. This is called a **thermocouple**. Thermocouples have somewhat greater power capacities than crystals, but their capacity is still very small compared with some other sources. Thermocouples are mainly used as heat measuring devices.

When **light** strikes the surface of a substance, it may dislodge electrons from their orbits around the surface atoms of the substance. This occurs because light has energy, the same as any moving force. Metallic substances are more sensitive to light than other substances. Voltage produced in this manner is referred to as a **photoelectric** voltage. A photocell's capacity is also very small. However, it reacts to light-intensity variations very quickly. This characteristic makes the photocell very useful in television cameras, burglar alarms, etc.

Friction is the last of the six ways to produce electron movement and is the **least** used. Only **5** of the ways can be used to cause a **current to flow** through a wire; friction cannot be used. Friction is an unavoidable method of producing electron movement. Under certain conditions a **static charge** is generated by two objects being rubbed together. Example, walking across carpet on a dry day and touching a grounded object releases the static charge that was built up. Static charges are often a problem causing radio interference. Explosions can be caused by ignition from a static spark.

THE BATTERY

In 1780 Luigi Galvani thought he had discovered an electrical source in animals. Galvani was conducting a class in anatomy at a University in Italy when he removed dissected frog legs from a salt solution and suspended them with a copper wire. Whenever he touched the frog legs with an iron scalpel, the muscles of the frog leg twitched. Galvani realized that electricity was being produced, he thought it came from the muscles of the frog leg.

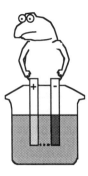

CURRENT FLOW

Alessandro Volta found that the muscles of the frog did not produce electricity. Volta discovered that the electricity was a result of a **chemical action** between the copper wire, iron scalpel, and the salt solution.

Volta went on to make the first **wet cell battery** as he found that by putting two **different metals** in certain chemical solutions, electricity could still be produced.

The simplest cell is known today as either a **galvanic** or **voltaic** cell in honor of these two men, Galvani and Volta.

Without having to dissect a frog, you can duplicate Galvani's experiment by substituting a lemon. Roll the lemon on a table to make it juicy. Then cut the top off the lemon. Insert a copper wire and a steel wire opposite each other in the top of the lemon. Just like a battery, one is positive and the other will be negative. Electricity will flow from one terminal to the other because of the **chemical action**.

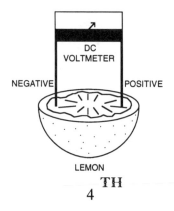

LEMON

TH

You can duplicate Volta's experiment using a stack of dimes and pennies. Separate the dimes and pennies with a piece of paper towel soaked in vinegar and water. Have **equal** number of dimes and pennies. If you start the stack with a dime, you should end with a penny. Add a tablespoon of vinegar to a glass of water for the solution. A DC meter connected to one end of the penny and dime on the other stack should show a brief deflection of the meter. The larger the stack, the greater the force.

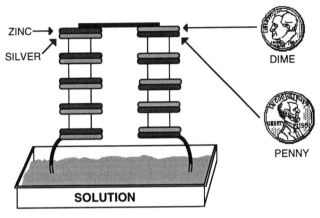

BATTERY TYPES

WET and DRY types
PRIMARY and SECONDARY types

A **cell** is a device that transforms chemical energy into electrical energy. The cell is the fundamental unit of the battery. A simple cell consists of two **electrodes** placed in a container that holds the **electrolyte**. Usually strips of **zinc and copper** metal are used for electrodes with **sulfuric acid** and water for the electrolyte.

CELL

NEG

POS

The **electrolyte** causes one electrode to lose electrons and develope a **positive charge**, and it causes the other electrode to build up a surplus of electrons and develope a **negative charge**. The difference between the two electrode charges is called the **cell voltage**. The cell is like a chemical furnace in which energy released by the zinc is transformed into electrical energy rather than heat energy.

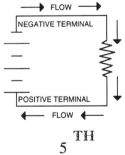

TH
5

The electrolyte may be salt, an acid, or an alkaline solution. An example would be the automobile storage battery, the electrolyte is in the **liquid form**; while in a **dry cell** battery, the electrolyte is a **paste**.

The dry cell is so called because its electrolyte is not in a liquid form. Actually, the electrolyte is a **moist** paste. If it should become dry, it would no longer be able to transform chemical energy to electrical energy. The name **dry** cell, therefore, is not strictly correct in a technical sense.

A cell that is not being used (sitting on the shelf) will gradually deteriorate because of slow internal chemical actions and changes in moisture content. This deterioration is generally very slow if the cells are stored properly in a cool area.

The **primary type** battery converts chemical energy to electrical energy directly, using the chemicals within the cell to start the action. An example would be a flashlight battery. Primary batteries are mostly used where a **limited current** is required.

PRIMARY
BATTERY

FLASHLIGHT
BATTERY

The **secondary type** battery must first be **charged** before it can convert chemical energy into electrical energy. An automotive battery is an example of a secondary battery as it **stores** the energy supplied to it. The secondary battery is generally used where a **heavy current** is required; secondary batteries are usually **wet** cells. The secondary type battery is referred to as the **storage battery**.

SECONDARY
BATTERY

AUTOMOTIVE
BATTERY

The **electron theory** is that current flows from **negative to positive**. Before the electron theory had been worked out it was believed that an electric fluid moved in a wire from positive to negative. This concept of current flow is called the **conventional current flow**. It doesn't matter which direction you choose as long as you are consistent when solving any circuit problem.

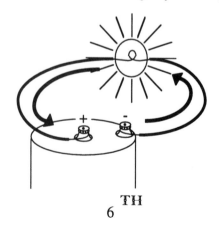

A lead-acid battery is constructed of a number of cells connected together, the number of cells needed depends upon the voltage desired.

A cell consists of a plastic or hard rubber compartment in which contains the cell element, consisting of two types of lead plates, known as positive and negative. These plates are insulated from each other by separators such as plastic, rubber or glass. The plates are submerged in a sulfuric acid solution, referred to as the electrolyte.

+ Positive

- Negative

The positive terminal marked (+) is slightly larger than the negative terminal marked (-).

The larger the area that the plates have, the more **current** the battery can supply. This rating is given in **ampere-hours**. If a battery is rated 100 ampere-hours, it means it will supply 5 amperes for 20 hours before the voltage will drop to a discharge level.

When the battery is in its charged condition, the active materials in the lead-acid battery are lead peroxide (used as the positive plate) and sponge lead (used as the negative plate). The electrolyte is a mixture of sulfuric acid and water. The strength (acidity) of the electrolyte is measured in terms of specific gravity.

Concentrated sulfuric acid has a specific gravity of about **1.830**; pure water has a specific gravity of 1.000. The acid and water are mixed in a proportion to give the desired specific gravity.

Specific gravity is the ratio of the weight of a given volume of electrolyte to an equal volume of pure water.

In a fully charged battery, all acid is in the electrolyte so that the specific gravity is at its maximum value. Overcharging does not change the water to more sulfuric acid. Instead, the water is lost as hydrogen and oxygen **gases**. These gases that escape through the vent holes are dangerous and explosive. When these gases are formed during overcharging, the electrolyte appears to be boiling.

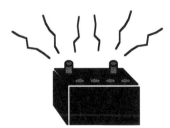

As a storage battery discharges, the sulfuric acid is depleted and the electrolyte is gradually converted into water.

The electrolyte that is placed in a lead-acid battery is usually 1.350 or less.

Not all liquids or materials have the same density. Sulfuric acid has a higher density than water. The density can be checked by seeing how a **hydrometer** floated in the electrolyte.

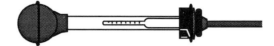

The hydrometer float consists of a hollow glass tube weighted at one end and sealed at both ends. A scale calibrated in specific gravity is laid axially along the body of the tube. The hydrometer float is placed inside the glass syringe and the electrolyte to be tested is drawn up into the syringe. When the syringe is held in a vertical position, the hydrometer float will sink to a certain level in the electrolyte. The reading on the stem at the surface of the liquid is the specific gravity of the electrolyte.

Most storage batteries use 80° F as a normal temperature to which specific gravity readings are corrected. To correct the specific gravity reading, add 4 points to the reading for each 10° F above 80° F and subtract 4 points for each 10° F below 80° F.

When water is added to a storage battery, the battery should be charged for at least **one hour** before a hydrometer reading is taken. This allows time for the electrolyte to mix.

Hydrometers should be flushed with clean water daily to prevent inaccurate readings.

SPECIFIC GRAVITY READINGS		
FROM	**TO**	**CHARGE**
1.260	1.280	**FULLY CHARGED**
1.230	1.250	75% charged
1.200	1.220	50% charged
1.170	1.190	25% charged
1.140	1.160	very little capacity
1.110	1.130	discharged

Persons working near batteries should always wear rubber gloves, a rubber apron, and protective goggles. If the electrolyte is spilled on the skin or clothing, the exposed area should be rinsed immediately with water.

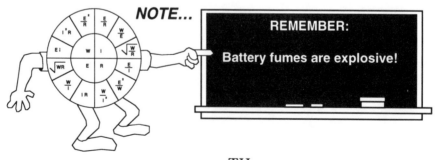

In the early days of electricity the only convenient source of electrical energy was the **voltaic cell.** Since cells and batteries were the only sources of power available, some of the early electrical devices were designed to operate from DC.

As the use of electricity became more wide spread, certain disadvantages in the use of DC became apparent. Example, to operate a 240 volt lamp, the DC generator must supply 240 volts. A 120 volt lamp could not be operated from this generator by any **convenient** means. A **resistor** would have to be placed in the circuit to reduce the 240 volts to 120 volts. A resistor would consume an amount of power equal to that consumed by the lamp. This is wasting electricity through the heat of the resistor.

Another disadvantage of DC is the large amount of power lost due to the **resistance** of the transmission wires on the towers from the generating plant. This loss can be greatly reduced by operating the transmission lines at a very **high voltage**. This is not practical with a DC generator because of the **commutator** which cannot handle high voltages.

AC generators can be built with much larger power and voltage ratings than DC generators.

AC voltage can be stepped up and down with a device called a **transformer**. Transformers cannot be used with DC.

A magnetic circuit is a complete path through which magnetic lines of force may be established under the influence of a magnetizing force. Most magnetic circuits are composed largely of magnetic materials in order to contain the magnetic flux. These circuits are similar to the **electric circuit**, which is a complete path through which current is caused to flow under the influence of an electromotive force.

Planet earth is a huge magnet and surrounding the earth is the magnetic field produced by earth's magnetism.

There are only two types of magnets: permanent magnets and electromagnets. A magnet is normally made of iron.

Think of magnetic materials as either hard or soft. Soft materials are used in devices where a change in the magnetic field is necessary in the operation of the device, sometimes a very rapid change is required. These are called electromagnets. An electromagnet can be activated by a switch; the magnetic field can be turned on and off by a switching action.

Hard materials are used for permanent magnets such as the magnet that holds a note on a refrigerator.

There are three fundamental conditions which must exist before a voltage can be produced by magnetism.

1. There must be a **conductor** in which the voltage will be produced.
2. There must be a **magnetic field** in the conductor's vicinity.
3. There must be a relative **motion** between the field and the conductor. The conductor must be moved so as to cut across the magnetic lines of force, or the field must be moved so that the lines of force are cut by the conductor.

When a conductor or conductors **move across** a magnetic field so as to cut the lines of force, electrons **within the conductor** are impelled in one direction or another. Thus, a voltage (force) is created. This is called a **generator**.

A generator converts **mechanical** energy into **electrical** energy. Whereas an electric motor is just the opposite, it uses electrical energy to perform a mechanical function. An example would be a fan.

The water falling from a dam is the mechanical energy used to drive a generator to produce electrical energy.

 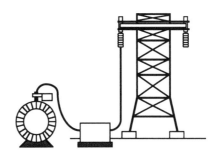

Whatever the orginal source of energy - water, coal, oil, gas, steam, the sun, the wind - the final step is always the conversion of **mechanical energy** from rotation of a generator to produce **electrical energy**.

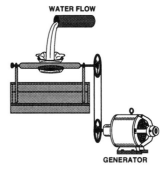

When a conductor is **moved** through a magnetic field in such a way that it cuts the lines of magnetic flux a force is applied to make **electrons move**. This is the basic principle of how an AC generator works.

Shown to the right is the simplest form of an AC generator. It consists of a single loop of wire, which is placed between the poles of a permanent magnet and made to **rotate**. As the loop of wire rotates, it cuts through the magnetic lines of force and a **voltage is developed**.

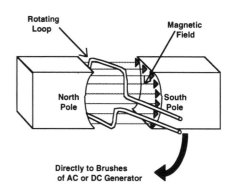

All generators, whether AC or DC consist of a rotating part and a stationary part. The rotating part of a DC generator is referred to as the **armature** . The coils that generate the magnetic field are mounted on the stationary part which is referred to as the **field**. In most AC generators the opposite is true, the field is mounted on the rotating part referred to as the **rotor**, and the armature is wound on the stationary part referred to as the **stator**.

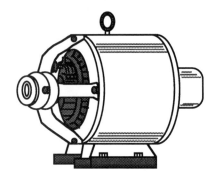

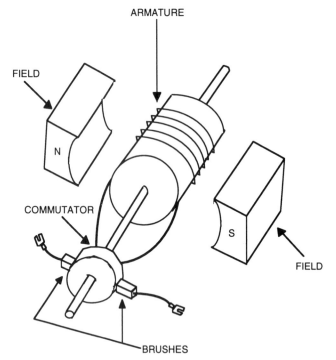

ARMATURE

FIELD

N

COMMUTATOR

S

FIELD

BRUSHES

The complete armature, the iron core, winding, commutator and shaft, is positioned inside an iron frame or housing. The field poles are made of iron, either solid or laminations and support coils of wire called field windings. The field winding is an electromagnet.

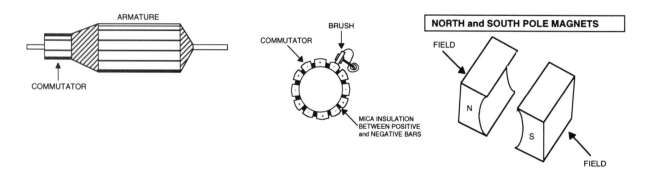

ARMATURE

COMMUTATOR

COMMUTATOR

BRUSH

MICA INSULATION BETWEEN POSITIVE and NEGATIVE BARS

NORTH and SOUTH POLE MAGNETS

FIELD

N

S

FIELD

When the armature revolves through the lines of flux, the magnetic energy forces current to flow in the wire. When the wire in the armature goes **down** the field current flows in **one direction**; but when the wire goes **up** the field, the current flows in the **other** direction.

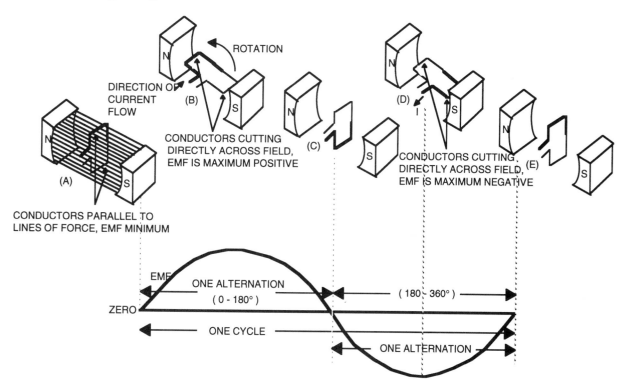

For a single loop rotating in a two-pole field (one-north pole and one-south pole) you can see that each time the loop makes one complete revolution the current **reverses direction twice**. A single hertz (cycle) will result if the loop makes one revolution each **second**. A complete cycle is 360°. There are **two alternations** in one complete cycle. One positive alternation and one negative alternation. This is called a **sine wave**. By reversing the direction twice in one cycle this is called **alternating current** (AC).

To convert AC to DC a switch must be operated twice for every cycle. If the generator output is alternating at 60 Hz (cycles), the switch must be operated 120 times per second to convert AC to DC. Obviously, it would be impossible to operate a switch manually at this high rate of speed.

A direct current generator (DC) uses a **commutator** to change the alternating current to direct current.

The carbon brush as it slides on the revolving commutator reverses the connections of the connection in the armature to the external circuit at the instant when the voltage of the conductors is zero and changing in direction. The commutator switches the wires outside the generator while the armature turns, thus keeping the current flow in the **same direction** at all times. If a commutator is not used, the current coming out of the generator will **change direction** as the armature turns.

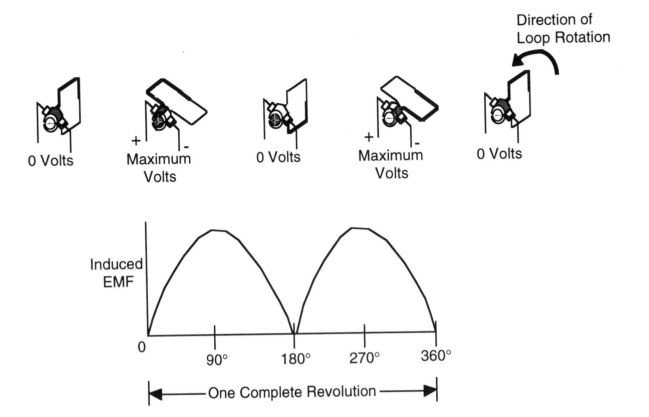

Direction of Loop Rotation

0 Volts   Maximum Volts (+ −)   0 Volts   Maximum Volts (+ −)   0 Volts

Induced EMF

0   90°   180°   270°   360°

One Complete Revolution

The brushes are positioned on **opposite** sides of the commutator so that they pass from one commutation half to the other at the instant the loop reaches the point in its rotation where the induced voltage reverses polarity. The brushes are effectively shorting the ends of the loop directly together. So instead of the output voltage reversing polarity after one-half revolution, the voltage output for the second half revolution is identical to that of the first half.

In a practical generator, the revolving loop of wire in the armature will contain several loops of wire cutting the magnetic flux of the fields.

When a coil or armature makes one complete revolution, it passes through 360 **mechanical degrees**, when an emf current passes through one cycle, it passes through 360 **electrical time degrees**.

If the generator makes two complete revolutions per second, the output frequency will be **two Hz** (cycles). In other words, the frequency of a two-pole generator happens to be the same as the number of revolutions (cycles) per second. As the speed is increased, the frequency is increased.

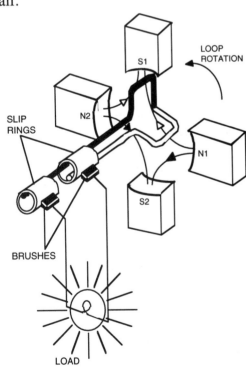

LOOP ROTATION

S1

SLIP RINGS

N2

N1

S2

BRUSHES

LOAD

There are only **two types** of generators, AC and DC. Over 90% of all electric power is AC. AC generators do not have commutators and this makes them far superior to a DC generator. AC generators are also called **alternators**, since they produce an **alternating current**.

AC generators can be built with much larger power and voltage ratings than DC generators. The reason is with the AC generator output connections are bolted directly to the stationary windings.

All generators operate on the same basic principle, a magnetic field cutting through conductors or conductors passing through a magnetic field.

There are two groups of conductors:

I. A group of conductors in which the output voltage is generated
II. A group of conductors through which direct current (DC) is passed to obtain an electromagnetic field of fixed polarity (excitation).

The conductors in which output voltage is generated are referred to as **armature windings**. The conductors in which the electromagnetic field originates are referred to as the **field windings**.

There must be a **motion** between the armature windings and the field windings. AC generators are built in two major assemblies, the **stator** and the **rotor**.

ARMATURE
ROTOR

FIELD
STATOR

There are two types of motion, either the revolving armature (rotor) or the revolving field (stator).

In the **revolving armature** AC generator, the stator provides a stationary electromagnetic field. The rotor acting as the armature, revolves in the field, cutting the lines of force, producing the desired voltage. In this generator, the armature output is taken through slip rings and thus retains its AC characteristic.

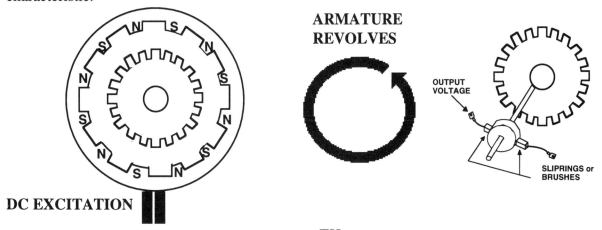

ARMATURE
REVOLVES

OUTPUT
VOLTAGE

SLIPRINGS or
BRUSHES

DC EXCITATION

The revolving armature AC generator is **seldom** used. Its primary limitation is the fact that its **output** power is conducted through sliding contacts, sliprings and brushes. The sliprings and brushes **limit the amount of voltage** that can be carried through them due to arcing and flashovers. Consequently, revolving armature AC generators are limited to low-power, low-voltage applications. An example would be an automobile alternator.

Remember you can just as easily rotate the **magnet assembly** (the fields). This is what the Yugoslavian Nikola Tesla developed and received patents on in 1888.

The **revolving field** AC generator is by far the most widely used today. In this type of generator, direct current from a separate source (excitation) is passed through windings on the rotor by means of sliprings and brushes. This maintains a rotating electromagnetic field of fixed polarity. The rotating magnetic field cuts through the armature windings imbedded in the surrounding stator. As the rotor turns, AC voltages are induced in the windings since magnetic fields of first one polarity and then another cut through them. Now here is the important part, since the output power is taken from **stationary windings**, the output may be connected through **fixed** terminals and not revolving sliprings or brushes that would limit high voltages. Sliprings and brushes are adequate for the DC field (excitation) supply because the power level in the field is much smaller than in the armature circuit.

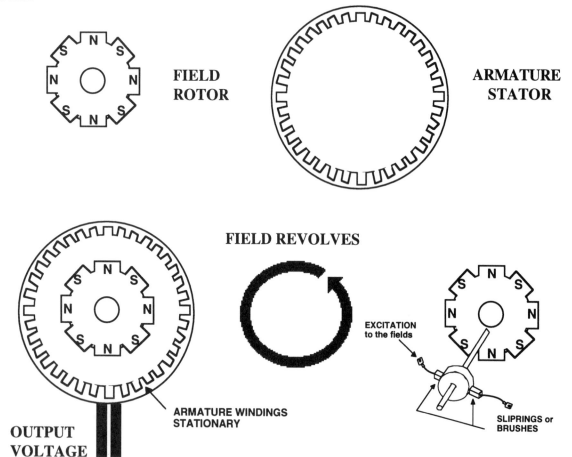

FIELD ROTOR

ARMATURE STATOR

FIELD REVOLVES

EXCITATION to the fields

SLIPRINGS or BRUSHES

ARMATURE WINDINGS STATIONARY

OUTPUT VOLTAGE

Fixed terminals on stationary winding allows higher voltages.

Excitation through the rotating fields is provided at lower voltages.

DC voltage changes are obtained by using series resistors which causes **low efficiency** due to heat loss.

DC generator rating are limited to relatively low voltage and power values as compared to AC generators.

AC armature stator voltages of 13,800 are common compared to 750 volts for a large DC generator.

The initial cost and the maintenance and repair costs for AC is considerably less than the costs for DC.

Although, there are a number of applications where **DC** either must be used or will do the job better than AC, such as:

• Charging of storage batteries
• Electronics
• Electroplating process
• Excitation of the field windings of generators
• Varible speed motors

There are special jobs that require **heavy starting torque** and **high rate of acceleration** such as locomotives and monorail trains which are driven by traction motors which require DC. Using DC motors in these applications eliminates the need for clutches, gear shifting transmissions, differential gearing, drive shafts and universal joints.

AC is changed to DC by **rectifiers** or **motor-generator** sets. Thus, the costly conversion to DC is needed only for certain applications.

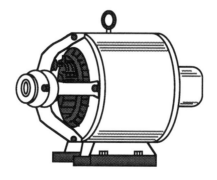

OHM'S LAW

In 1827 George Simon Ohm discovered some laws relating to the strength of a current in a wire. Ohm found that electricity acts like **water** in a pipe. The law was so simple that it was not believed. Ohm was forced to resign his professorship and live in obscurity until he was recognized 14 years after his discovery.

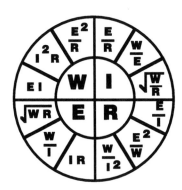

Ohm's Law is one of the most important things that you will use throughout your electrical career. It is a mathematical tool which is of the greatest use in determining an **unknown** factor of voltage, current or resistance in an electrical circuit in which the other two factors are known.

It is a simple law that states the relationship between voltage, current and resistance in a mathematical equation.

In electrical terms, voltage is represented by the letter "E" (electromotive force), current by the letter "I" (intensity), and resistance by the letter "R".

The Ohm's Law formula cannot work properly unless all values are expressed in the **correct units** of measurement:

> **VOLTAGE is always expressed in VOLTS**
> **CURRENT is always expressed in AMPERES**
> **RESISTANCE is always expressed in OHMS**

We measure electromotive force in volts, we measure electric current in amps, and we measure resistance in ohms.

Electricity has many more terms that have to do with measurement: **"VOLTS, "AMPS", "OHMS", "WATTS"** and more.

We must first understand how the electrical system functions and then mathematical analysis can follow.

Since you cannot visually **see** the flow of electrons, current, etc. and you need to **see** the relationship between voltage, current, and resistance, let's do it with some **terms** which you are more familiar with, using **water**.

WATER	ELECTRICITY
PUMP	GENERATOR
PIPE	CONDUCTOR
PRESSURE	VOLTAGE
FLOW OF GALLONS	AMPERES
RESTRICTION	RESISTANCE

The **generator** is like a **water pump**, the prime mover.

The **conductor** is like the **water pipe**, the larger the conductor, the less the resistance and the more flow.

The **voltage** is like the **water pressure**, the force pushing.

The **amperes** are like the **flow of water**, an amount of current flowing is like the gallons per minute in water.

The **resistance** is like the **restriction** in the water pipe. A reduction in the water pipe size would cause opposition to the amount of gallons per minute, as would the resistor in an electrical circuit. It limits the flow of current.

Watts (power) is expressing the **rate of work** involved; the power required. With water it requires more work to pump water up to a water tower than it would to pump water at ground level. Wattage is the rate at which the electrical energy is changed into another form of energy, such as light or heat. The faster a lamp changes electrical energy, the brighter it will be.

Horsepower (hp) is the unit of measurement for mechanical power which is equal to 33,000 foot-pounds per minute. One horsepower is developed when the product of the distance and pounds equals 33,000 and this is done in one minute. In electrical terms, one horsepower = **746 watts**. One horsepower is developed if 33,000 pounds are lifted one foot in one minute. This represents the **work** done by the **output** of a motor.

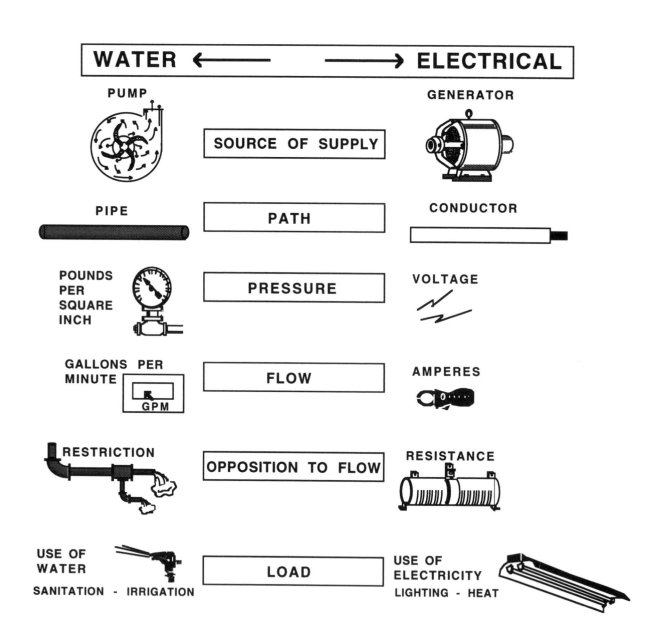

WATER ⟵ ⟶ ELECTRICAL

| PUMP | SOURCE OF SUPPLY | GENERATOR |

| PIPE | PATH | CONDUCTOR |

| POUNDS PER SQUARE INCH | PRESSURE | VOLTAGE |

| GALLONS PER MINUTE GPM | FLOW | AMPERES |

| RESTRICTION | OPPOSITION TO FLOW | RESISTANCE |

| USE OF WATER SANITATION - IRRIGATION | LOAD | USE OF ELECTRICITY LIGHTING - HEAT |

| HIGH-PRESSURE CUTOUT SWITCH | PROTECTION | CIRCUIT BREAKER - FUSE |

(E) VOLT: The practical unit of voltage; the pressure required to force one ampere through a resistance of one ohm. To make electrons flow in a conductor, an electrical pressure must be applied and this is called electromotive force (EMF) or voltage.

(I) AMPERE: The practical unit of electric current flow; the electric current that will flow through one ohm under a pressure of one volt.

(Ω) OHM: The practical unit of electrical resistance; the resistance through which one volt will force one ampere.

(R) RESISTANCE: The opposition which a device or material offers to the flow of current; the opposition which results in the production of heat in the material carrying the current. Resistance is measured in ohms. All resistances have two dimensions: cross-sectional area and length.

(W) POWER: The rate at which electrical energy is delivered and consumed. Power is measured in watts. A motor produces mechanical power measured in horsepower. A heater produces heat (thermal) power. A light bulb produces both heat and light power (usually measured in candlepower).

Electrical power is equal to voltage times the amperage. $\mathbf{W = E \times I}$

Ohm's Law states: In a DC circuit, the current is directly proportional to the voltage and inversely proportional to the resistance. In other words, the water flowing in a pipe (amperage) will be increased if the water pressure (voltage) is increased. And, if the restriction (resistance) in the pipe is **less**, the water flow (amperage) will be **more**.

Get into the habit of always sketching out an Ohm's Law circuit **before** you begin trying to solve it.

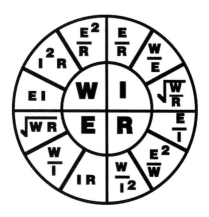

$I = E/R$ One volt will force one amp through a conductor having a resistance of one ohm.

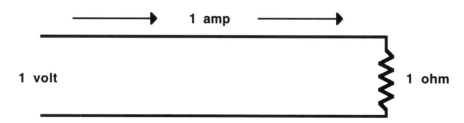

$I = E/R$ If the voltage is increased to 2 volts, the current will be 2 amps through one ohm of resistance.

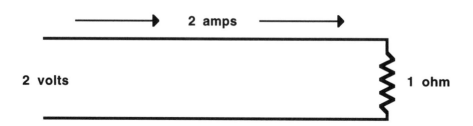

$I = E/R$ If the voltage is increased to 10 volts, the current will be 10 amps through one ohm of resistance.

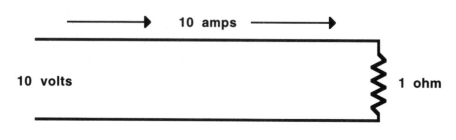

$\boxed{\mathbf{I = E/R}}$ If the resistance is **reduced** to 1/2 ohm, the current would double to 20 amps, if the voltage remained at 10 volts.

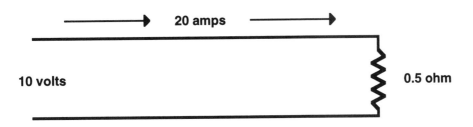

Directly proportional means that one factor will be **increased** in proportion to an **increase** in another factor.

Example: The current **increased** to 2 amps as the voltage **increased** to 2 volts, the resistance remained the same, one ohm.

Inversely proportional means that one factor will be **increased** in proportion to a **decrease** in another factor or vice versa.

Example: The current will **increase** in proportion to a **decrease** in resistance. The current doubled to 20 amps with a decrease in resistance to 0.5 ohm.

Doubling the cross-sectional area of a conductor will reduce the resistance of the conductor by one-half.

An electric circuit consists of a complete path for the current from the supply, through the load, and back to the supply. If the current can't get back to the source of supply, it will never leave.

NOTE...

Kirchhoff's First Law:
The sum of all the currents flowing toward a junction always equals the sum of all the currents flowing away from that junction.

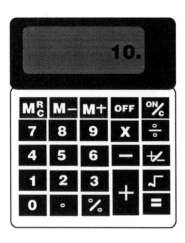

Before using the Ohm's Law circle the student must understand how to use the formulas and the calculator.

To solve W, the circle shows three ways: EI, I²R or E²/R.

EI means E x I, example: 120 volts x 10 amps = 1200 watts.
I²R means 10 amps x 10 amps x 12 ohms = 1200 watts.
E²/R means 120 volts x 120 volts divided by 12 ohms = 1200 watts.

E = √WR means 1200 watts x 12 ohms = 14400. √‾ is the symbol for square root. Square root means times itself equals. On your calculator you should have a √‾ button. After taking 1200 watts times 12 ohms and getting 14400 showing in your calculator, now press the √‾ button and the correct answer of 120 volts will appear. Which means 120 x 120 = 14400. So the square root of 14400 is 120.

To solve I = √W/R, first divide 1200 watts by 12 ohms = 100. Now press the √‾ button, = 10 amps. The square root of 100 is 10. 10 x 10 = 100.

NOTE...

The student MUST understand how to use the formulas!

R = E² W

24 ᵀᴴ

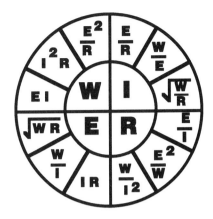

The Ohm's Law circle is divided into four parts: I = amperes; R = resistance in ohms; E = voltage; W = watts (power).

THE AMPERE: The ampere is the unit of electric current. It is the amount of current which will flow through a resistance of 1 ohm when a potential of 1 volt is applied across the resistance.

THE OHM: The ohm is the unit of resistance. It is the amount of resistance which will permit 1 ampere to flow at a potential difference of 1 volt.

THE VOLT: The volt is the unit of electromotive force, or electric potential. It is that potential which will cause a current of 1 ampere to flow through a resistance of 1 ohm.

THE WATT: The watt is the unit of electrical power. In direct-current circuits the power in watts is the product of the voltage times the current.

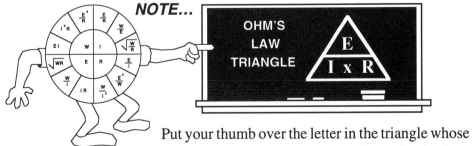

Put your thumb over the letter in the triangle whose value you want to find and the formula for calculating that value is given by the two remaining letters.

The student must be able to use the circle to solve the unknown. Let's divide the circle into four parts and work examples using all the formulas.

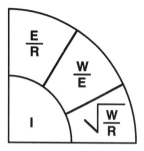

I = E/R

Example: What is the current in amperes flowing in a circuit that has a voltage of 120 and a resistance of 10 ohms?

Solution: I = E/R = 120v/10 ohms = **12 amperes**.

I = W/E

Example: What is the current in amperes flowing in a circuit that has a 1440 watt load and a voltage of 120?

Solution: I = W/E = 1440w/120v = **12 amperes**.

I = √ W/R

Example: What is the current in amperes flowing in a circuit that has a 1440 watt load and a resistance of 10 ohms?

Solution: I = √ W/R = 1440w/10ohms = 144 √ 144 = **12 amperes**.

TO FIND RESISTANCE

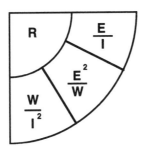

$$R = W/I^2$$

Example: What is the resistance in ohms for a circuit that has a load of 1440 watts and a current in amperes of 12?

Solution: $R = W/I^2 = 1440w/144a$ (12a x 12a) = **10 ohms**.

$$R = E^2/W$$

Example: What is the resistance in ohms for a circuit that has a voltage of 120 and a load of 1440 watts?

Solution: $R = E^2/W = 120v \times 120v = 14400/1440w = $ **10 ohms**.

$$R = E/I$$

Example: What is the resistance in ohms for a circuit that has a voltage of 120 and a current of 12 amps?

Solution: $R = E/I = 120v/12a = $ **10 ohms**.

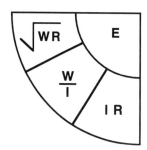

$$\boxed{E = \sqrt{W \times R}}$$

Example: What is the voltage of a circuit that has a load of 1440 watts and a resistance of 10 ohms?

Solution: $E = \sqrt{W \times R}$ = 1440w x 10 ohms = 14400 $\sqrt{14400}$ = **120 volts**.

$$\boxed{E = W/I}$$

Example: What is the voltage of a circuit that has a load of 1440 watts with 12 amps of current?

Solution: E = W/I = 1440w/12a = **120 volts**.

$$\boxed{E = I \times R}$$

Example: What is the voltage of a circuit that has 12 amps flowing with a resistance of 10 ohms?

Solution: E = I x R = 12a x 10 ohms = **120 volts**.

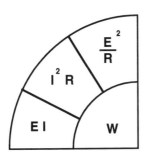

$$\boxed{W = E \times I}$$

Example: What is the wattage of a circuit that has a voltage of 120 with 12 amps of current flowing?

Solution: $W = E \times I = 120v \times 12a =$ **1440 watts**.

$$\boxed{W = I^2R}$$

Example: What is the wattage of a circuit that has a current flowing of 12 amps and a resistance of 10 ohms?

Solution: $W = I^2R = 12a \times 12a = 144 \times 10$ ohms $=$ **1440 watts**.

$$\boxed{W = E^2/R}$$

Example: What is the wattage of a circuit that has a voltage of 120 and a resistance of 10 ohms?

Solution: $W = E^2/R = 120v \times 120v = 14400/10$ ohms $=$ **1440 watts**.

Examples of Ohm's Law applied to solve everyday situations:

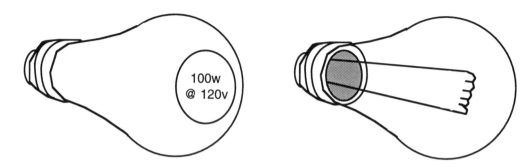

A 100 watt @ 120v light bulb is 100 watts **if** you apply **exactly** 120 volts. If the voltage is **less** than 120 volts, the watts will be less than 100. If the voltage is **more** than 120, the watts will be **more** than 100. The **key** to the first step is to find the **fixed resistance** of the bulb. This bulb was built with a fixed resistance so when you apply exactly 120 volts you will have exactly 100 watts. If the voltage is higher or lower, the wattage and current will also be higher or lower. The fixed resistance will remain the same.

Example: If you purchased a 100w @ 120v light bulb and installed it in a table lamp which had a voltage of only 115v, what is the wattage of the light bulb?

Solution: First step find the **fixed resistance**, R = E^2/W = 120v x 120v/100w = 144Ω. W = E^2/R = 115v x 115v/144Ω = **91.84 watts**.

Example: Have you ever had an electric heat unit in which the output air was warm but not really hot. Check the name plate for kw and volts, now check the **actual** voltage supplying the unit. If the nameplate on the unit reads 10 kw @ 240v and the source to the unit is only **208 volts**, what is the actual kw output?

Solution: First step find the **fixed resistance**, R = E^2/W = 240v x 240v/10,000w = 5.76Ω. W = E^2/R = 208v x 208v/5.76Ω = 7511w. 7511w/1000 = **7.511 kw**.

SERIES CIRCUIT

An electric circuit is a complete path through which electrons can flow from the negative terminal of the voltage source, through the connecting wires, through the load or loads, and back to the positive terminal of the voltage source. A complete circuit is made up of a voltage source, connecting wires, and the effective load.

If the circuit is arranged so that the electrons have only **one possible path**, the circuit is called a **series circuit**.

In a series circuit all devices are connected end to end, in a closed path, and the **same** amount of current flows through each device.

If two or more resistances are connected in such a way that they carry the **same** current, they are in **series**.

The series circuit was used in the old-style Christmas lights. Each bulb was rated at 15 volts when used on a 120 volt circuit of eight lights. Each bulb received one-eighth of the total 120 volts or 15 volts. If one bulb burns out, they all go out. Series circuit wiring is impractical for ordinary purposes.

Example: What is the current flowing in this series circuit?

R1   6 ohms

120 volts

R2   6 ohms

Solution: The first step is to find the resistance in the series circuit. The **total** resistance is equal to the **sum** of the individual resistances.

Total resistance in series : R total = R1 + R2

6 ohms + 6 ohms = 12 ohms

Now apply the Ohm's Law formula for current: I = E/R

E = 120 volts   120v/12Ω = **10 amps current flowing**.

Since there is but **one** path for current to flow in a series circuit, the same current must flow through each part of the circuit. To determine the current throughout a series circuit, only the current through **one** of the loads need be known.

Example: With 6 amps of current flowing in this series circuit, what is the applied voltage?

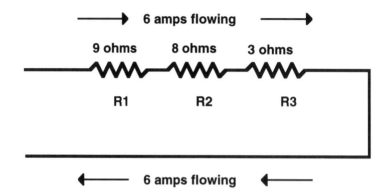

Solution: The first step is to find the total resistance. In a series circuit the formula for total resistance is: R1 + R2 + R3 + ... $9\Omega + 8\Omega + 3\Omega = 20 \, \Omega$ R total.

Now apply the Ohm's Law formula: E = I x R The current is 6 amps x 20 ohms = **120 volts**. 120 is the applied voltage to this series circuit.

In the basic series circuit with only **one** resistor the voltage drop across the resistor is the total voltage across the circuit and is equal to the applied voltage. In a series circuit with **more** than one resistor, the total voltage drop is also equal to the applied voltage, but consists of the sum of two or more individual voltage drops. In any series circuit the **sum** of the resistor voltage drops must equal the source voltage.

This can be proven with the three resistor series circuit shown above. Voltage drop = I x R. 6 amps x 9 Ω = 54 volts dropped, it takes 54 volts to force 6 amps through a 9 ohm resistor. 6 amps x 8 Ω = 48 volts dropped. 6 amps x 3 Ω = 18 volts dropped. Total voltage drop = 54v + 48v + 18v = 120 volts. But, remember even though this voltage is used to push the load through the resistors and it drops from 120 volts to zero volts, the voltage is replaced every **1/60 th of a second** in a 60 cycle system.

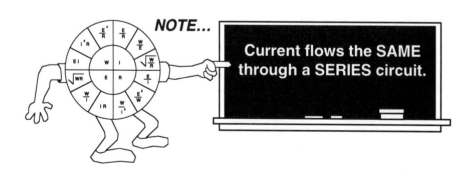

Example: With 11.5 amps flowing in this series circuit, what is the total resistance?

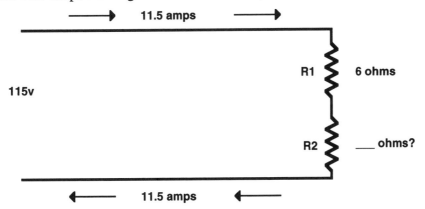

Solution: Apply Ohm's Law formula R = E/I = 115v/11.5a = 10 ohms   R total = **10 ohms**.

Example: What is the resistance of R2?

Solution: 10 ohms R total - 6 ohms R1 = **4 ohms R2**.

Example: What is the voltage at R1?

Solution: Apply Ohm's Law formula E = I x R = 11.5a x 6Ω = **69 volts**.

Example: What is the voltage at R2?

Solution: Apply Ohm's Law formula E = I x R = 11.5a x 4Ω = **46 volts**.

•Checkpoint: 69 volts + 46 volts = 115 volts (the applied voltage).

Current flows the same in series. It takes 115 volts to push 11.5 amps through 10 ohms of resistance.

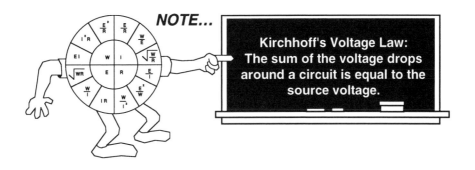

Each of the resistors in a series circuit consumes power which is dissipated in the form of heat. The total power (watts) must be equal in amount to the power consumed by the circuit resistors. In a series circuit the total power is equal to the **sum** of the wattage dissipated by the individual resistances.

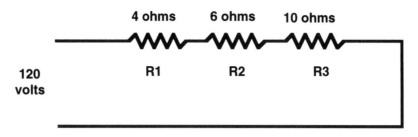

$W = E^2/R$ 120v x 120v = 14400   R = total resistance $4\Omega + 6\Omega + 10\Omega = 20\Omega$ Rtotal 14400/20Ω = **720 watts**.

What is the current flowing in this series circuit? $I = E/R = 120v/20\Omega = $ **6 amperes**. Current flows the same through a series circuit.

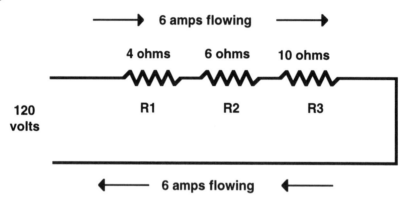

The wattage consumed at R1 is $W = I^2R = 6$ amps x 6 amps x 4Ω = **144 watts.**
The wattage consumed at R2 = 6 amps x 6 amps x 6Ω = **216 watts**.
The wattage consumed at R3 = 6 amps x 6 amps x 10Ω = **360 watts**.
Total consumed wattage = 144w + 216w + 360w = **720 watts**.

SUMMARY SERIES CIRCUIT

•**The same current flows through each part of a series circuit.**
•**The total resistance is equal to the sum of individual resistances.**
•**The total voltage across a series circuit is equal to the sum of individual voltage drops.**
•**The voltage drop across a resistor is proportional to the size of the resistor.**
•**The total power dissipated is equal to the sum of the individual power dissipations.**

Ohm's Law can be applied to a branch circuit to show how resistance, current and voltage react when changes are made in the circuit. The 20 amp branch circuit has #12 solid copper wires, the receptacle is located 40 feet from the panelboard which would be 80 feet of wire.

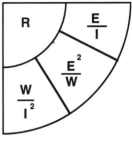

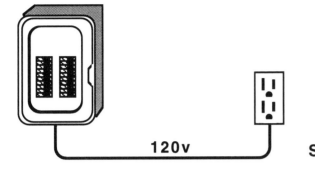

120v

Sweeper draws 5 amps

To find the resistance of the sweeper load, $R = E/I = 120v/5a = 24\Omega$.

The wire from the panelboard to the receptacle also has a resistance. A #12 solid copper wire has a resistance of 1.93Ω for 1000 feet. To find the resistance for 80' of wire multiply $1.93\Omega \times .080' = .1544\Omega$ resistance in the 80' of wire.

Total resistance of the circuit with the sweeper running would be $24\Omega + .1544\Omega = 24.1544\Omega$.

To find the current flowing in the circuit, $I = E/R = 120v/24.1544\Omega = 4.96$ amps.

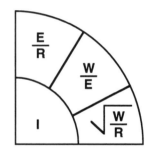

To show how resistance effects current, a short circuit occurs between the branch circuit wires in the box at the receptacle. The short circuit by-passes the 24Ω resistance in the sweeper, so the circuit resistance is $.1544\Omega$ total. Now calculate the amount of current flowing through the wires back to the circuit breaker, $I = E/R = 120v/.1544\Omega = \textbf{777 amperes}$.

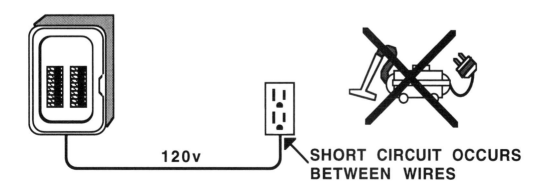

120v

SHORT CIRCUIT OCCURS BETWEEN WIRES

The 20 amp rating of the branch circuit is thermal current, not the destructive high currents that occur during a ground-fault or short-circuit condition. Electrical conductors and equipment have current withstand ratings generally based on the overcurrent device (fuse or circuit breaker) opening the circuit within the first one-half cycle, which is 8 thousandths of a second. The ICEA lists the maximum short-circuit withstand rating for a #12 copper wire at **3800 amperes** for one-half cycle. A #12 copper wire can withstand 1550 amperes for 3 cycles, but remember 60 cycles is still only **one second** in time.

Many electricians don't realize that a 20 amp rated circuit with #12 conductors must be capable of carrying thousands of amperes of current during a fault.

Example, the branch circuit cable is accidentally cut 6 feet from the panelboard thus practically eliminating the resistance of the circuit. The only resistance is 12 feet of wire. 1.93Ω x .012' = .02316Ω. Current flow, I = E/R = 120v/.02316Ω = **5181 amperes.**

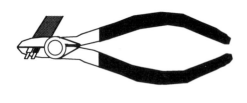
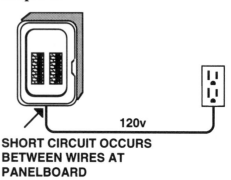

**SHORT CIRCUIT OCCURS
BETWEEN WIRES AT
PANELBOARD**

If the short-circuit occurred inside the panelboard with only 6 feet of wire. Resistance would be 1.93Ω x .006' = .01158Ω. Current flow, I = E/R = 120v/.01158Ω = **10,362 amperes.**

That's why the circuit breaker has an interrupting rating stamped on the side **10,000 amperes.**

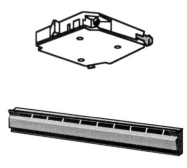

Example, the current flowing through an electric heater at a **high** resistance creates heat. The voltage (pressure) is pushing the flow of current through the high resistance. When a short-circuit fault occurs it offers a **new path** of **less resistance** so the voltage (pressure) doesn't have to push as hard and the current **flow** increases tremendously as there is no opposition (resistance) to its flow.

The high current will open the inverse-time circuit breaker quickly. Inverse-time means, the higher the current the quicker it will open.
Opening the circuit breaker is like shutting off the water pump, the pressure is turned off.

Now you can see how the steel in your pliers melts when you cut into a hot circuit. Steel melts at approximately 2500° F. Remember, 20 amps flowing in a circuit won't melt steel. As you can see by using Ohm's Law, we are talking about much higher currents than the 20 amperes for a #12 wire.

PARALLEL CIRCUIT

A parallel circuit is a circuit having **more than one path** for current to flow from a common voltage source.

SERIES CIRCUIT HAS ONLY ONE PATH

PARALLEL CIRCUIT HAS MORE THAN ONE PATH

The old-style Christmas lights were connected in series. The current had only one path to flow as the lights were connected end to end in series. If one light bulb burnt out the entire circuit was opened.

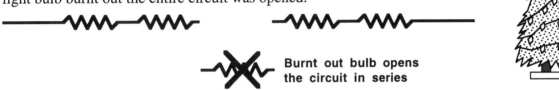

Burnt out bulb opens the circuit in series

In parallel the lights are connected **side-by-side** instead of end-to-end so that there exists more than one path through which current can flow.

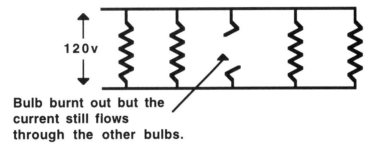

120v

Bulb burnt out but the current still flows through the other bulbs.

In a series circuit a **portion** of the source voltage is dropped across each series load and the sum of these individual voltage drops is equal to the source voltage.

When resistances in parallel are connected across a voltage source, the **voltage** across each of the resistors will always be the same. However, the **entire** source voltage is dropped across each load. This is the reason that all parallel loads are connected directly across the voltage source.

When a series circuit becomes short-circuited the resistance of the other loads in series keep the circuit resistance from dropping to zero. Parallel circuits develop **larger** damaging short circuit currents because each parallel load is connected directly across the source voltage. If any one of the parallel loads becomes shorted, it drops the resistance between the load and the source to practically zero.

The **current** through each resistor will vary depending on the size of each individual resistor.

In a parallel circuit, loads having **low resistance** draw **more** current than loads having high resistance.

Parallel circuits have two types of current flow, **total current flow** and the current flow through each **individual** load.

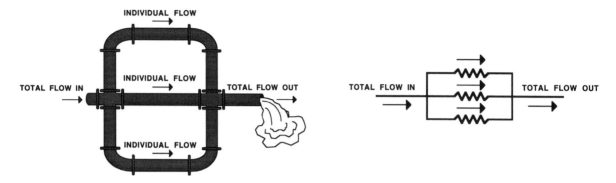

To calculate the current flowing in a parallel circuit start by calculating the current flow in **one** load.

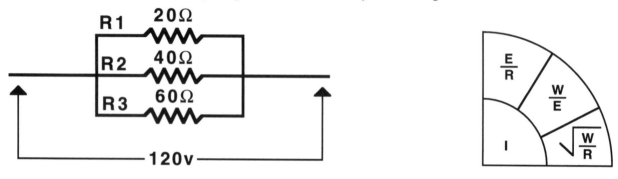

$I = E/R$ The current flowing through R1 = 120v/20Ω = 6 amperes.
The current flowing through R2 = 120v/40Ω = 3 amperes.
The current flowing through R3 = 120v/60Ω = 2 amperes.

The **total current** in parallel is equal to the **sum** of all the individual load currents.
$I1 + I2 + I3 = I$ total   6 amperes + 3 amperes + 2 amperes = 11 amperes.

The total current flow in is 11 amperes and the total current flow out is 11 amperes. The 11 amperes is divided up between three individual loads as it flows through the parallel circuit.

NOTE...

The total CURRENT in parallel is the current of each load added COLLECTIVELY.

In a **series** circuit the total resistance was solved by adding all of the individual resistances together. The more resistances there are, the more the total resistance would be.

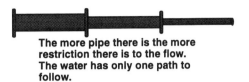

The more pipe there is the more restriction there is to the flow. The water has only one path to follow.

In a parallel circuit the **total** resistance is **less** than the size of the smallest load. And, everytime you **add** another load to the circuit the **total** resistance will be **less**.

As an apprentice this was very difficult for me to understand. I had learned in math that everytime you add another amount the total is more!

Let's put these words into a **picture** and **see** how it is easy to understand.

Each time a pipe (load) is **added** the total restriction (resistance) is **less**. By adding another pipe you create another path for the flow. With the addition of a another pipe you have more flow (amperage), the only way you can have more flow (amperage) is to have less restriction (resistance).

EQUAL PARALLEL RESISTANCES

The simplest calculation for total resistance in a parallel circuit is when all of the loads are **equal** in resistance.

When two pipes of equal size are combined together (paralleled) the two together have twice the cross-sectional area. They could, therefore, be replaced with one pipe and it would double the cross-sectional area.

The same is true with conductors. By paralleling two conductors together the resistance of one conductor is cut in half because the cross-sectional area has doubled.

Doubling the area of a conductor will reduce the resistance of the conductor by one-half.

Example: Parallel two #500 kcmil THW conductors, 1000 feet in length, and find the total resistance in parallel.

.0258 ohm

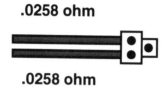

.0258 ohm

Solution: Use NEC Table 8 = #500 kcmil resistance 0.0258 per m/ft for each conductor, when connecting the two #500 kcmil conductors in parallel, you would have a total circular-mil area of 1000 kcmil. NEC Table 8 shows a resistance for #1000 kcmil at 0.0129 ohms per m/ft.
• Checkpoint: Apply the formula for total resistance in parallel for **equal** resistors.

$$\frac{\text{Resistance of one}}{\text{Number of resistors}} \quad = \quad 0.0258\Omega/2 \text{ resistors} = \mathbf{0.0129\Omega} \textbf{ total resistance in parallel}.$$

EQUAL PARALLEL RESISTANCES

$$\frac{\text{TOTAL RESISTANCE}}{\text{IN PARALLEL}} = \frac{\text{RESISTANCE OF ONE}}{\text{NUMBER OF RESISTORS}}$$

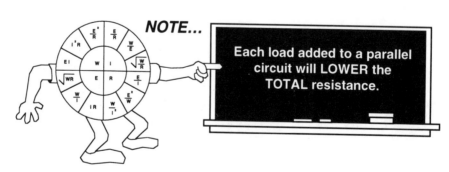

In practical wiring applications we are connecting our lighting circuits in parallel.

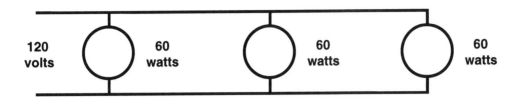

Example: What is the total current in this parallel circuit?

Solution: Apply Ohm's Law formula I = W/E = 60w/120v = 0.5 amp per light. I total = I1 + I2 + I3 = 0.5a + 0.5a + 0.5a = **1.5 amps total current in parallel**.

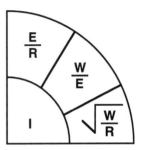

Example: What is the resistance of one light?

Solution: Apply Ohm's Law formula $R = E^2/W$ = 120v x 120v/60w = **240 ohms each light**.

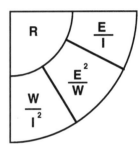

Example: What is the total resistance of this parallel circuit?

Solution: Use the formula for **equal** resistors in parallel $240\Omega/3$ resistors = **80 ohms R total**.

EQUAL PARALLEL RESISTANCES

TOTAL RESISTANCE =   RESISTANCE OF ONE
IN PARALLEL   NUMBER OF RESISTORS

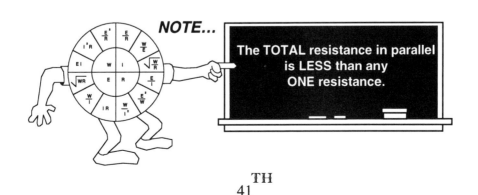

NOTE...

The TOTAL resistance in parallel is LESS than any ONE resistance.

When a circuit contains resistors in parallel with different unequal values, the problem of solving the total resistance becomes more difficult.

There are different formulas for **unequal** parallel resistors you can apply, both giving the same results.

$1/Rt = 1/R1 + 1/R2 + 1/R3 \ldots$

Example: What is the total resistance of this parallel circuit?

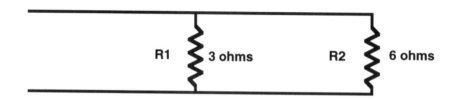

$1/Rt = 1/3\Omega + 1/6\Omega$ the common denominator is 6.
$2/6 + 1/6 = 3/6$ now invert $6/3 =$ **2 ohms total resistance**.

The other formula to find total resistance **unequal** in parallel is: $\dfrac{R1 \times R2}{R1 + R2}$

$R1 = 3$ ohms $R2 = 6$ ohms $\dfrac{3\Omega \times 6\Omega}{3\Omega + 6\Omega} = \dfrac{18}{9} =$ **2 ohms total resistance**.

By using either formula you will get the **same** answer, 2 ohms total R, which is **less** than any one resistance.

NOTE...

AGAIN..... The checkpoint is:
The TOTAL resistance in parallel
is LESS than any
ONE resistance.

Example: What is the total resistance for **three unequal** resistors in parallel?

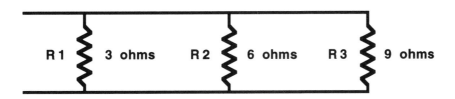

Solution: Use the formula 1/Rt = 1/R1 + 1/R2 + 1/R3. To find the common denominator multiply R1 x R2, if R3 will divide **evenly** that will be the common denominator. 3 x 6 = 18/9 =2 (divides evenly).

$$\frac{1}{3} + \frac{1}{6} + \frac{1}{9}$$ 18 is the common denominator

$$\overline{18} + \overline{18} + \overline{18}$$

$$\frac{6}{18} + \frac{3}{18} + \frac{2}{18} = \frac{11}{18}$$ invert to 18/11 = **1.63 ohms total resistance.**

Now apply the other formula for **unequal parallel**. For 3 resistors the formula would be:

$$\frac{R1 \times R2 = Y}{R1 + R2} \qquad \frac{Y \times R3 = Rt}{Y + R3}$$

R1 = 3   R2 = 6   R3 = 9

$$\frac{3 \times 6 = 18 = 2}{3 + 6 \quad 9} \qquad Y = 2 \qquad \frac{2 \times 9 = 18 = \textbf{1.63 ohms total resistance.}}{2 + 9}$$

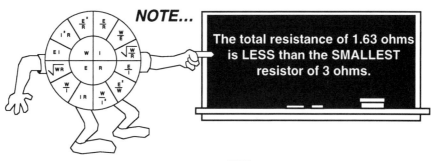

NOTE...

The total resistance of 1.63 ohms is LESS than the SMALLEST resistor of 3 ohms.

43TH

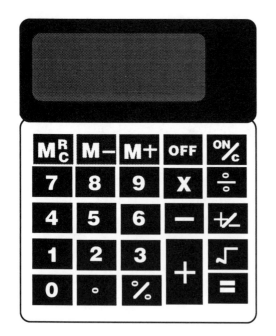

Here is another way to find the total resistance in parallel for unequal resistors using your **calculator**.

Let's use the same resistors 3 Ω, 6 Ω and 9 Ω and see if we get the same answer of 1.63 Ω R total.

Simply follow these steps:

OHMS 44

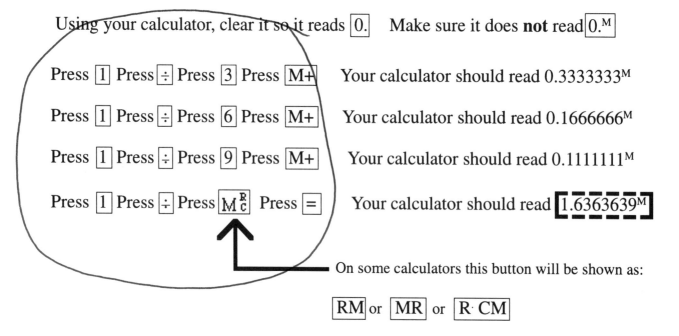

Using your calculator, clear it so it reads $\boxed{0.}$ Make sure it does **not** read $\boxed{0.^M}$

Press $\boxed{1}$ Press $\boxed{÷}$ Press $\boxed{3}$ Press $\boxed{M+}$ Your calculator should read 0.3333333^M

Press $\boxed{1}$ Press $\boxed{÷}$ Press $\boxed{6}$ Press $\boxed{M+}$ Your calculator should read 0.1666666^M

Press $\boxed{1}$ Press $\boxed{÷}$ Press $\boxed{9}$ Press $\boxed{M+}$ Your calculator should read 0.1111111^M

Press $\boxed{1}$ Press $\boxed{÷}$ Press $\boxed{M_C^R}$ Press $\boxed{=}$ Your calculator should read $\boxed{1.6363639^M}$

On some calculators this button will be shown as:

$\boxed{RM}$ or $\boxed{MR}$ or $\boxed{R\cdot CM}$

The numbers $\boxed{3}\boxed{6}\boxed{9}$ are for the unequal resistors of 3 Ω, 6 Ω, and 9 Ω. By using your calculator you can calculate the total resistance for as many resistors as the circuit would have by simply following this format. The **final step** is always :

Press $\boxed{1}$ Press $\boxed{÷}$ Press $\boxed{M_C^R}$ Press $\boxed{=}$ Your calculator should read the **ANSWER.**

Practice this calculator drill a few times, it can be very helpful in determining total resistance in a parallel circuit with **unequal** resistors.

Example: Find the total resistance in this parallel circuit having **four unequal** resistors.

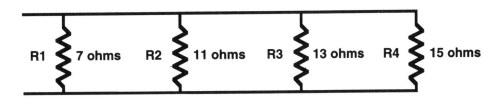

Solution: $1/Rt = 1/R1 + 1/R2 + 1/R3 + 1/R4$ Find the common denominator 7 x 11 x 13 x 15 = 15,015. The common denominator is 15,015.

$$\frac{1}{7} + \frac{1}{11} + \frac{1}{13} + \frac{1}{15}$$

$$\frac{2145}{15015} + \frac{1365}{15015} + \frac{1155}{15015} + \frac{1001}{15015} = \frac{5666}{15015}$$ invert 15015/5666 = **2.65 ohms total resistance**

Using the other formula:

$$\frac{R1 \times R2 = Y}{R1 + R2} \qquad \frac{Y \times R3 = Z}{Y + R3} \qquad \frac{Z \times R4 = Rt}{Z + R4}$$

$R1 = 7$ $R2 = 11$ $R3 = 13$ $R4 = 15$

$$\frac{7 \times 11 = 77}{7 + 11 \ \ 18} = 4.28 \qquad Y = 4.28 \qquad \frac{4.28 \times 13 = 55.64}{4.28 + 13 \ \ 17.28} = 3.22 \qquad Z = 3.22 \qquad \frac{3.22 \times 15 = 48.3}{3.22 + 15 \ \ 18.22} = 2.65\Omega$$

R total = 2.65 ohms.

Now follow your caculator drill from the preceding page, you should match the same answer **2.65Ω.**

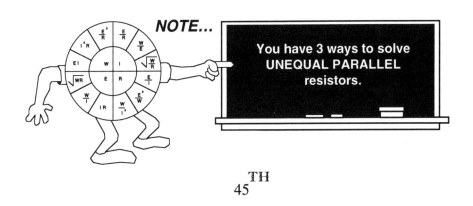

NOTE...

You have 3 ways to solve
UNEQUAL PARALLEL
resistors.

In a parallel circuit the total wattage is **equal** to the sum of the wattage dissipated by the individual resistances, same as in a series circuit.

Example: to find the total wattage in the parallel circuit below there are several ways to calculate the power.

$$W = E \times I$$
$$I = E / R \qquad 120v/20\Omega = 6a$$
$$120v/30\Omega = 4a$$
$$120v/40\Omega = 3a$$

I total = 6a + 4a + 3a = 13 amps

Total wattage = 120 volts x 13 amps = **1560 watts**

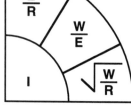

The wattage in each branch = I^2R and then add the branches.
R1 = 6a x 6a x 20Ω = 720 watts
R2 = 4a x 4a x 30Ω = 480 watts
R3 = 3a x 3a x 40Ω = 360 watts
$$\overline{\textbf{1560 watts}}$$

120v

R1   20 ohms   R2   30 ohms   R3   40 ohms

SUMMARY PARALLEL CIRCUIT

•The total current is equal to the sum of the branch currents.
•The total resistance is less than any one individual resistance.
•The voltage across each branch is the same as the source voltage.
•The total power consumed is equal to the sum of the individual power dissipations.

A series-parallel circuit is a combination of both a series and a parallel circuit. Some parts of the circuit are connected in series and some parts are connected in parallel.

In order to analyze the circuit you must be able to **recognize** which parts are connected in series and which parts are connected in parallel. With some circuits it will be easy to recognize how it's connected. With other circuits it will be more difficult and you will have to **redraw** the circuit and put it in the **simplest form**.

Here are some reminders that we have already learned.

SERIES CIRCUIT HAS ONLY ONE PATH   **PARALLEL CIRCUIT HAS MORE THAN ONE PATH**

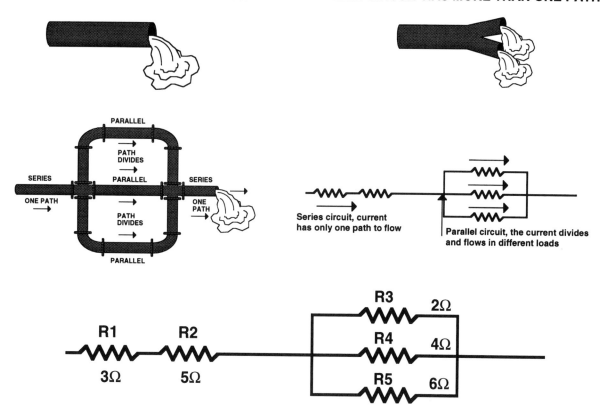

To find the **total resistance** of this series-parallel circuit start at the end of the circuit and calculate the resistance of R3, R4 and R5 that are connected in parallel.

$$\frac{2\Omega \times 4\Omega}{2\Omega + 4\Omega} = \frac{8}{6} = 1.33 \quad \frac{1.33 \times 6\Omega}{1.33 + 6\Omega} = \frac{7.98}{7.33} = 1.088 \text{ or } \mathbf{1.09 \text{ total resistance parallel}}.$$

Now R3, R4 and R5 have been reduced to their simplest form of **one resistor** with a resistance of 1.09Ω.

Reduced to simplest form

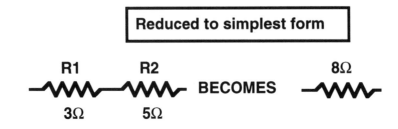

R1 and R2 are connected in series so they would **add** together for a total resistance in series of 3Ω + 5Ω = **8Ω total series resistance.**

Reduced to simplest form

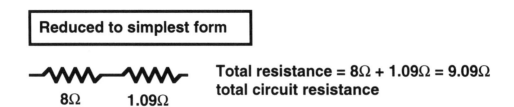

Reduced to its simplest form the circuit now looks like this:

Reduced to simplest form

Total resistance = 8Ω + 1.09Ω = 9.09Ω total circuit resistance

Example: Find the total resistance in this series-parallel circuit.

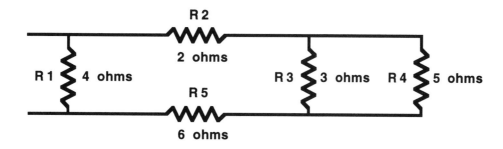

Solution: When trying to solve total resistance in a series-parallel circuit always start at the **end** of the sketch. R4 is connected in parallel with R3 so find the resistance of these two.

$$\frac{R3 \times R4}{R3 + R4} = \frac{3 \times 5}{3 + 5} = \frac{15}{8} = 1.875 \text{ ohms (combined resistance of R3 and R4)}$$

Now the circuit looks like this:

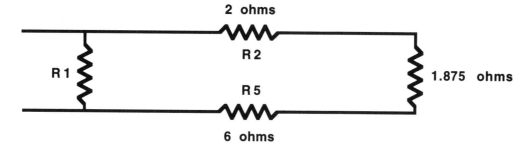

1.875 ohms is in series with R2 and R5. Series resistance adds together, $1.875\Omega + 2\Omega + 6\Omega = 9.875\Omega$.

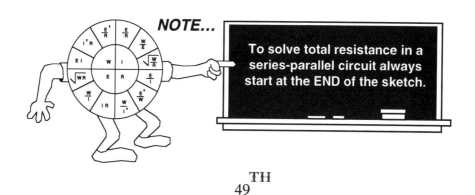

NOTE...

To solve total resistance in a series-parallel circuit always start at the END of the sketch.

The circuit now looks like this:

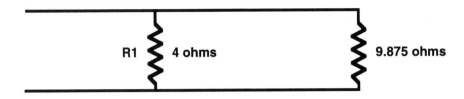

9.875 ohms is in parallel with R1. $\dfrac{9.875 \times 4}{9.875 + 4} = \dfrac{39.5}{13.875}$ = **2.84 ohms total resistance**.

In practical wiring applications we use series-parallel connections for heating elements in cooking units to obtain different heat selections.

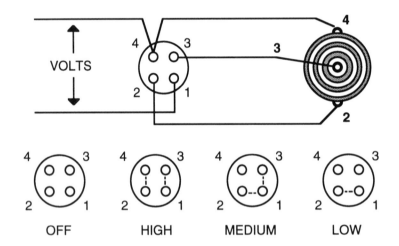

OFF   HIGH   MEDIUM   LOW

The heating element is connected to a special control switch 240/120v which allows different wattages to be obtained by different switch positions.

The series-parallel element would look like this in a sketch:

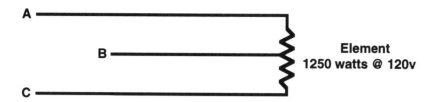

A

B

C

Element
1250 watts @ 120v

Example: Find the fixed resistance of the cooking element.

Solution: Use Ohm's Law formula $R = E^2/W = 120v \times 120v/1250w =$ **11.52 ohms fixed resistance**.

   For **high heat** 240volts would be applied through wires A and C through the special control switch.

High heat wattage : $W = E^2/R = 240v \times 240v/11.52\Omega =$ **5000 watts**.

   For **medium heat** 120 volts would be applied through wires A and B. Now you are using half of the resistance, 5.76 ohms, by tapping from wire B.

Medium heat wattage: $W = E^2/R = 120v \times 120v/5.76\Omega =$ **2500 watts**.

   For **low heat** 120 volts would be applied through wires A and C. Now you are using the full resistance 11.52 ohms at the low voltage 120.

Low heat wattage: $W = E^2/R = 120v \times 120v/11.52\Omega =$ **1250 watts**.

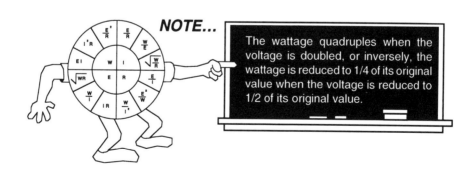

NOTE...

The wattage quadruples when the voltage is doubled, or inversely, the wattage is reduced to 1/4 of its original value when the voltage is reduced to 1/2 of its original value.

There are two types of series loads.

I. Two or more resistances in one branch of the circuit as shown below. R2 and R3 are in series with each other and in parallel with R1.

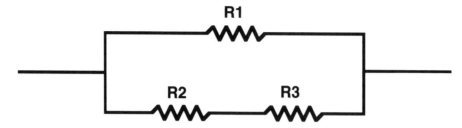

II. Any resistance through which the total current flows as shown below. All of the current would flow through R4.

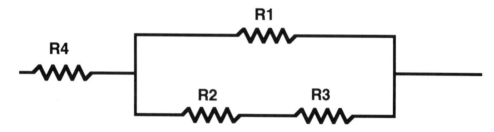

The same circuit can be drawn in different forms as shown below. Either way R1 carries all the current, then the current divides between R2 and R3, R3 and R4 are connected in series and in parallel with R2.

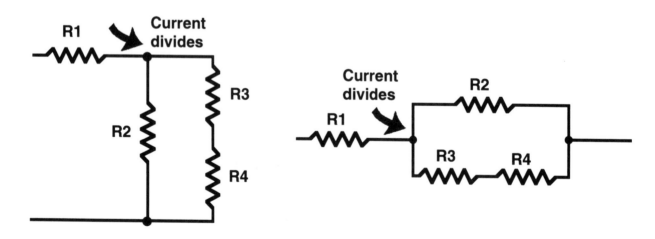

The series-parallel circuit shown below shows that R1 carries the full current and then the current divides into two paths. R2 and R3 are connected in series together and connected in parallel with R4.

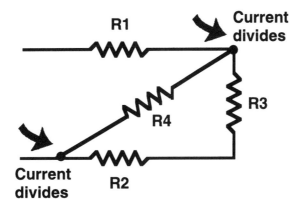

This same circuit can be redrawn into a simpler form. R1 is in series carrying the full current. R2 and R3 are connected in series and in parallel with R4.

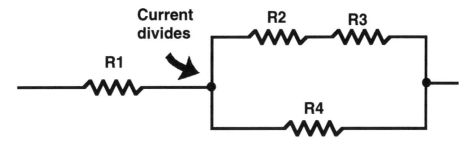

Calculate the total resistance of the series-parallel circuit below.

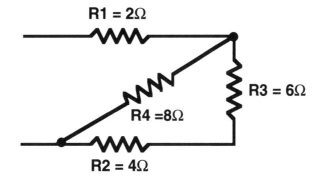

R2 and R3 are in series $4\Omega + 6\Omega = 10\Omega$.
Now this 10Ω load is in parallel with R4, $\quad \dfrac{10\Omega \times 8\Omega = 80}{10\Omega + 8\Omega = 18} = 4.4\Omega$

These are now combined into a 4.4Ω load which is in series with R1.
$4.4\Omega + 2\Omega = \textbf{6.4}\Omega$ **total resistance**.

Find the total resistance in the series-parallel circuit shown below.

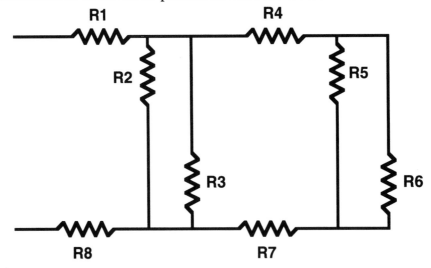

R6 is connected in parallel with R5. R4, R5 and R7 are connected in series. R2 and R3 are connected in parallel. R1 and R8 are in series as they both would carry the full current. This circuit can be redrawn as shown below.

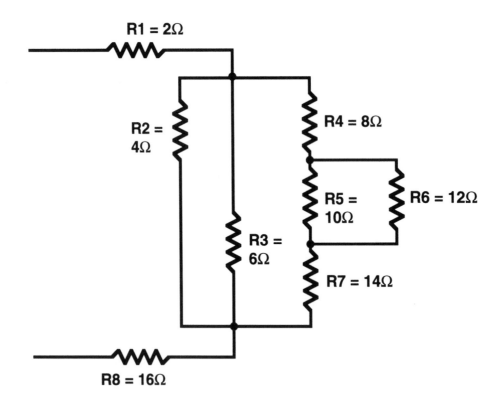

To find the total resistance of this series-parallel circuit start at the end of the circuit with the R5 and R6 connected in parallel.

$$\frac{12\Omega \times 10\Omega = 120}{12\Omega + 10\Omega = 22} = 5.45\Omega \text{ resistance of R5 and R6 connected in parallel now is called Rx}$$

Now the end of the circuit looks like this:

The 3 loads are in series, $8\Omega + 5.45\Omega + 14\Omega = 27.45\Omega$

R4 = 8Ω

Rx = 5.45Ω   =   Rx = 27.45Ω

R7 = 14Ω

Next calculate the parallel resistance of R2, R3 and Rx.
$$\frac{4\Omega \times 6\Omega = 24}{4\Omega + 6\Omega = 10} = 2.4\Omega \text{ resistance of R2 and R3 in parallel.}$$

$$\frac{2.4\Omega \times 27.45\Omega = 65.88}{2.4\Omega + 27.45\Omega = 29.85} = 2.21\Omega$$

R2   R3   Rx   =   2.21Ω

Rz

Now R1 and R8 are in series with Rz. $2\Omega + 16\Omega + 2.21\Omega = \mathbf{20.21\Omega}$ **total resistance.**

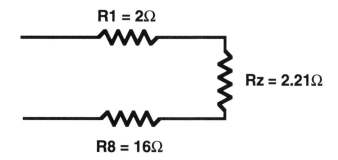

R1 = 2Ω

Rz = 2.21Ω

R8 = 16Ω

ADVANTAGES OF HIGHER VOLTAGES

The **higher** the voltage on a transmission line, the more efficient it is. Power is watts, W = E x I.

Wattage can be produced by several combinations of voltages and currents. Example: you can produce 1000 watts of power from 200 volts and 5 amps of current flow, or from 500 volts and 2 amps of current flow, or from 1000 volts and 1 amp of current flow.

When a current flows through a wire which contains resistance, there is a **power loss** in the wire. Power loss is wasted energy, power loss = I^2R. Any reduction in the amount of current flow required to transmit power results in a reduction of power loss in the transmission lines.

Example: to produce one megawatt (1,000,000 watts) you can have 6900 volts with 145 amps of current flow (6900v x 145a = 1,000,500w) or the AC voltage can be stepped up to 360,000 volts with 2.78 amps of current flow (360,000v x 2.78a = 1,000,800w).

In most electric circuits power loss is very low because the resistance of the wire is very low. The exception to this are the wires on transmission lines from the power plant to the user. These wires can run for **hundreds of miles** in length. Even large diameter copper conductors have a considerable amount of resistance when hundreds of miles are used.

If the resistance is doubled, the power loss is doubled; but if the current is doubled, the power loss would be **quadrupled**. The best way to **reduce** power loss is to **lower the current**.

Example: Power loss = I^2R, 20 amps of current flows through 10 ohms of resistance would equal 4000 watts of power loss. If the resistance was doubled to 20 ohms, 20 amps x 20 amps x 20 ohms = 8000 watts of power loss, twice as much when the resistance is doubled. But, if the current was doubled to 40 amps, 40 amps x 40 amps x 10 ohms = 16,000 watts of power loss, **four times** greater than the original 4,000 watts.

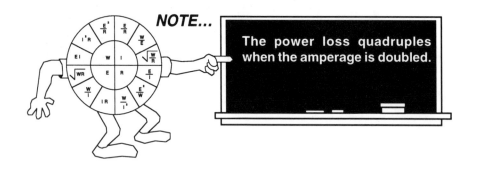

NOTE...

The power loss quadruples when the amperage is doubled.

You can see it is very important to keep the current flow at a low value in transmission lines. By raising the voltage to high levels, the current flow is very low thus reducing the power loss in the conductors.

Power loss = I^2R

Example:

6900 volt line 100 amps x 10 ohms Power loss = 100,000w	69,000 volt line 10 amps x 10 ohms Power loss = 1,000w

The 6900 volt line has **100 times** the power loss of the same line at 69,000 volts.

By using AC, large amounts of power can be sent over long distances without large losses along transmission lines. With DC this cannot be done.

The electrical devices used to raise and lower voltages are called **transformers**.

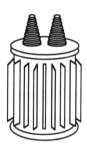

NOTE... By raising the voltage the current is lowered.

THE AC SINE WAVE

In building construction we use **alternating current (AC)** rather than DC. Alternating current changes direction at regular intervals of time. A 60 cycle alternating current changes **direction** 120 times every second; 60 positive and 60 negative alternations every second.

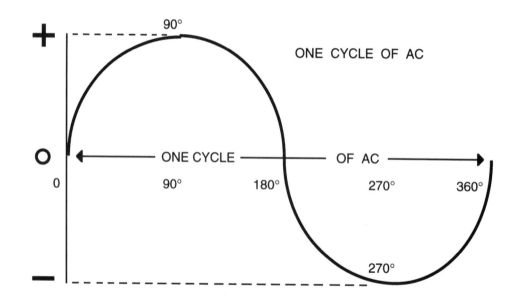

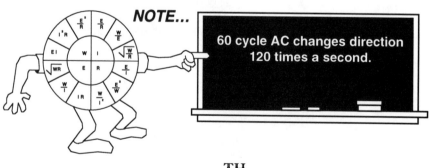

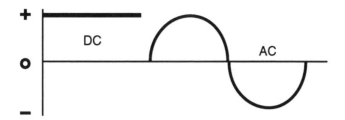

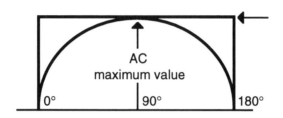

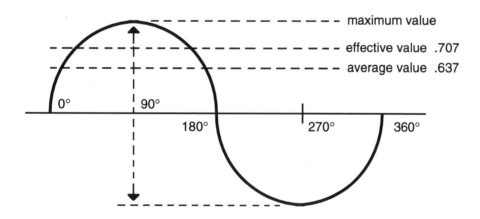

There are two maximum or peak values for each complete cycle of AC. Usually AC **voltages** and **currents** are expressed in **root mean square** (RMS) or **effective values**.

When DC or AC flows through a resistance, electric energy is converted into **heat**. AC varies continuously between maximum values and zero and is lower than DC.

The AC circuit will have to be increased to 1.414 amperes before it will produce the **same heating effect** as will one ampere of DC current. Similarly, the peak voltage is 1.414 times the RMS voltage.

RMS VALUE = MAXIMUM x .707	MAXIMUM VALUE = RMS/.707

Peak Maximum

RMS Effective Value .707

METER READS
RMS EFFECTIVE VALUE

The RMS effective value is the **same** as the DC maximum value. RMS is .707 (or approximately 70%) of the AC maximum peak. AC maximum peak is an **instantaneous value** changing 60 times a second. The AC alternator is producing a sinusoidal (sine curve) waveform.

Alternating voltage or current changes continuously with time. It rises from zero to a maximum value in one direction and decreases back to zero. It then rises to the same maximum value in the opposite direction and again decreases to zero. These values are repeated again and again at equal intervals of time.

Root-mean-square current is the abbreviated form of "the square root of the mean of the square of the instantaneous currents".

By the AC reversing 60 times a second, the volt or ammeter is **not** reading the peak to peak (maximum), the meter is reading the RMS (effective value) which is .707 or 70% of maximum.

METER READS
RMS EFFECTIVE VALUE

The RMS value is used to compare the AC heating effects to the DC heating effects.

The effective value (RMS) of an AC voltage or current is the value that will cause the **same** amount of **heat** to be produced in a circuit containing only resistance that would be caused by a DC voltage or current of the same value.

 **339 volts**
240 volts

If the RMS (effective value) is 240 volts, the maximum (peak) voltage of an AC system is 339v.

240v/.707 = **339 volts**

240 volts of DC will produce the same effect as 339 volts AC.

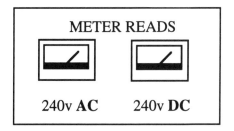

Example: If the maximum value of an AC current is 50 amps, the RMS value would be approximately _____ amps.

(a) 25   (b) 30   (c) 35   (d) 50

Solution: 50 amps x .707 = 35.35 or **35 amps.**   The ammeter would read 35amps

Two lamps, one is 6 volts (RMS) supplied from an AC transformer, the other lamp is a 6 volt DC supplied from a battery. The identical lamps will have the same brightness showing the effect of the two voltages are the same and the power (watts) in both circuits are the same. •Remember, the AC is 6 volts (RMS), the maximum (peak) voltage would be 6v/.707 = **8.48 volts** to give this **same** effect.

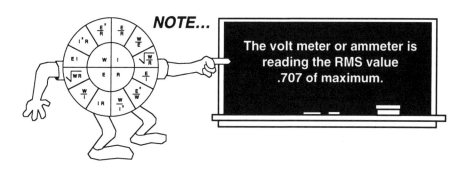

The term **"in phase"** is the portion of a cycle or period through which the current or voltage has passed since going through zero value at the beginning of the cycle or period. Phase is abbreviated: ∅.

IN PHASE

Picture two roller coaster's with cars "volts" and "amps". If the two cars start together and finish together, they are "in phase".

IN PHASE

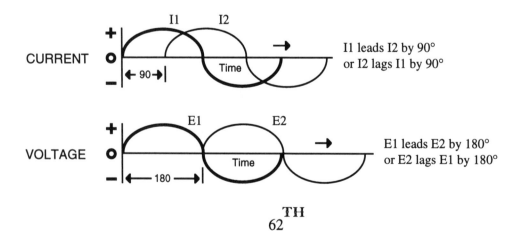

same magnitude   different magnitude

This condition occurs in an AC circuit that contains only **resistance**. When the circuit is "in phase", Power (watts) = E x I. This is called **true power**.

Since many of the loads supplied by AC have induction, such as motors, transformers, etc., the current is **out-of-phase** with the voltage.

CURRENT   I1 leads I2 by 90°
or I2 lags I1 by 90°

VOLTAGE   E1 leads E2 by 180°
or E2 lags E1 by 180°

In circuits containing inductance or capacitance, the power in **volt-amperes (va)** usually is more than the power in watts. This is called **apparent power**.

Apparent power is "floating power" because it does no work. Apparent power is called **reactive power**.

Reactive volt-amperes (va) denote energy and **not** power. Reactive volt-amperes represent energy supplied to the circuit during part of a cycle and returned to the system during the time when the system inductance is discharging.

To find **true power (watts)** multiply the volt-amperes (va) by the **power factor**.
W = E x I x PF

Power factor (PF) is the ratio between true power in **watts** and the apparent power in **volt-amps**.
PF = watts/volt-amps

Power factor is also given by the ratio of resistance to impedance. The power factor angle is the angle **theta** (cosine of theta).

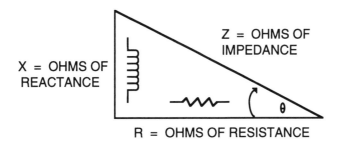

The power factor angle is between R and Z in the diagram above.

When "in phase" the power factor is **unity 1.0**.

True power produces light in a lamp filament, reactive power merely surges back and forth in the circuit.

To reduce excessive **apparent power** demands, power companies try to keep power factor as close to unity (1.0) as possible.

A low power factor may be due to a **lagging** phase angle caused by inductive circuits. This can be corrected by using capacitors in the circuit whose **leading** phase angle will cancel out the inductive lag.

If the power factor is low because of a **leading** (capacitive) phase angle, as with fluorescent lamps, it may be corrected by using inductors (ballasts) in the circuit.

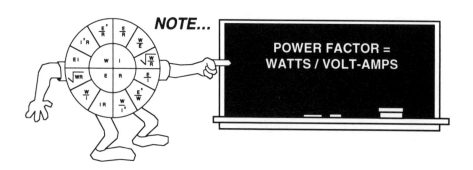

NOTE...

POWER FACTOR =
WATTS / VOLT-AMPS

The Ohm's Law formulas we have been applying are for DC or AC circuits having **ohmic resistance** only.

In AC circuits, **ohmic resistance** is a resistance imposed by incandescent lamps or resistance type heating.

Only a few circuits can accomplish their purpose with **resistance** only. To ring bells, operate relays, and drive motors, the loads require **coils** for the driving force. A force that causes electrical energy to be converted into mechanical energy and mechanical energy into some form of work.

When a **coil** of wire is in a circuit we have **inductance**. Inductance is a property of an electric circuit that **opposes** any change in the **current** through that circuit. In formulas, the letter "L" represents inductance. Inductance is measured in **henrys**.

The difference between a resistive circuit and an inductive circuit is the current flow in a resistive circuit changes **immediately** when the applied voltage is changed. In an inductive circuit current flow is **delayed** with respect to a change in applied voltage.

A coil of wire carrying a current acts as a magnet. AC is continuously changing so the circuit inductance affects AC current flow at all times.

$$\text{\_mmm\_} = \text{L} = \text{INDUCTANCE}$$

NOTE...

The letter "L" represents INDUCTANCE.

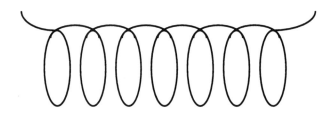

As the current rises in a single coil, an expanding magnetic field is established and an increasing number of lines of force cut across the turns of the coil. This in turn **induces** a counter EMF in the coil that **opposes** the increase in the current and causes it to rise more **slowly** than it would without the magnetic field.

In AC circuits we have inductance by the winding of a wire on a steel core in ballasts, motors, transformers, electromagnetics, etc.

A transformer is an electromagnetic device that transfers electrical energy. When the primary coil is excited it becomes magnetically coupled with the secondary coil with an alternating flux. Voltages will be **induced** in the secondary coil.

Inductance is a form of **reactance**. The other form of reactance is **capacitance**. Capacitance is a property of an electric circuit that **opposes** any change in the **voltage** across that circuit. The letter "C" represents capacitance. Capacitance is measured in **farads**.

Capacitance is the ability to receive and retain an electrical charge. It is defined as the charge (in coulombs) per volt.

When a capacitor is connected in an AC circuit, the plates become charged, then discharged, then charged again in the opposite direction, in rapid sequence with an **alternating** polarity of the applied voltage. The alternating current is said to flow "through" the capacitor. Because of the **insulating dielectric** no current can actually flow "through" the capacitor. The current **surging** back and forth gives the same effect as "flowing through".

NOTE...

The letter "C" represents CAPACITANCE.

The current in a capacitive circuit goes through its peak value **before** the applied voltage goes through its peak value.

Current in a capacitive circuit **leads** the applied voltage in time. In an inductive circuit current **lags** the voltage.

This can best be remembered by the statement **"ELI THE ICE MAN"**.

"ELI"   **E** = voltage   **L** = inductance   **I** = current

When you see the letter "L" you can say "E" leads "I" in an inductive circuit.

"ICE"   **I** = current   **C** = capacitance   **E** = voltage

When you see the letter "C" you can say "I" leads "E" in a capacitive circuit.

In an AC circuit, if we increase the **capacitance** a lamp will glow **brighter**. When we increase the **inductance** the lamp glows **dimmer**.

THE TWO FORMS of REACTANCE

INDUCTIVE (a coil)   CAPACITIVE (a capacitor)

The letter "X" represents reactance. Reactance is measured in **ohms**.

XL = inductive reactance   XC = capacitive reactance

When induction and capacitance are of **equal** values in a circuit, they **neutralize** each other, allowing only resistance to oppose the flow of current. This is called **resonance**.

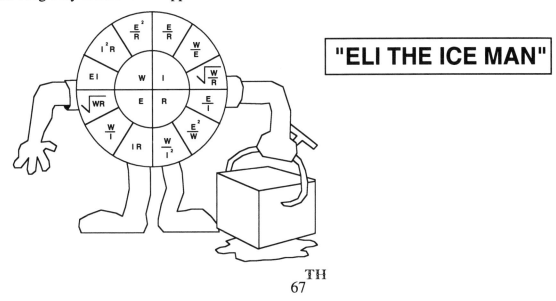

"ELI THE ICE MAN"

IMPEDANCE

The **total** opposition to the flow of current in an AC circuit is called **impedance**. The impedance of an AC circuit compares with the resistance of a DC circuit. The letter "Z" represents impedance. Impedance is measured in **ohms**.

IMPEDANCE = INDUCTION + CAPACITANCE + RESISTANCE

There are four classes of AC circuits:

1. Resistance only
2. Resistance and inductive reactance
3. Resistance and capacitive reactance
4. Resistance, inductive reactance, and capacitive reactance

There is some degree of reactance in all AC circuits (in some AC circuits the reactance is so small that it is negligible).

The reactance must be combined with the ohmic resistance to determine the impedance (Z).

The impedance of an AC circuit is equal to the square root of the sum of the square of the **resistance** and the **net reactance**.

Thus: $Z = \sqrt{R^2 + X^2}$

Ohm's Law can be applied to an AC circuit by substituting the ohms of the **total impedance** (induction + capacitance + resistance) for the ohms resistance in DC, Ohm's Law: $E = I \times Z$.

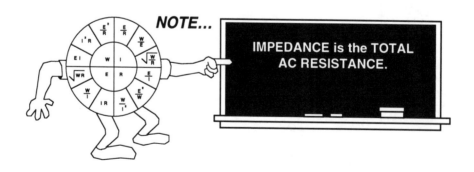

NOTE...

IMPEDANCE is the TOTAL AC RESISTANCE.

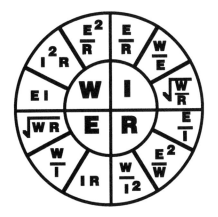

The Ohm's law circle actually applies to DC (direct current) pure resistance. AC (alternating current) has two components not found in a DC circuit that add opposition to the normal flow. These two components are called "inductive reactance" and "capacitive reactance".

As we have learned in theory, when an electric current moves through a wire, a magnetic field is formed around this wire. When the current in an electric circuit changes, the circuit may **oppose** the change. The property of the circuit that opposes the change is called **inductance**.

For a DC circuit, inductance affects the current flow when the circuit **is turned on or off**. When the switch is turned on, current flows through the circuit and the lines of magnetic force expand outward around the circuit conductors and the current rises from zero to its maximum value. Whenever a current flow changes, the induced magnetic field changes and opposes the change in current, whether it be an increase or decrease and inductance will **slow down** the rate at which the change occurs. When the switch is opened in a DC circuit, the current will drop very rapidly towards zero causing the magnetic field to collapse and generate a very high voltage, which not only opposes the change in current but can also cause an arc across the switch.

The big difference, is an AC circuit is **constantly** switching on and off, reversing direction 60 times a second. So circuit inductance affects AC circuits **all the time**.

In an inductive circuit when current increases, the circuit stores energy in the magnetic field. When current decreases, the circuit gives up energy from the magnetic field. In an AC circuit, the magnetic field is always changing. Every circuit has some inductance, although it may be so small that its effect is negligible, even in an AC circuit.

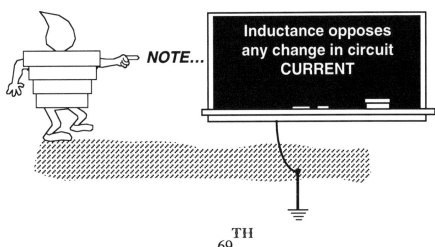

Every complete circuit has some inductance. Even the simple complete loop circuit or a single-turn coil has inductance. The coil having many turns has a higher inductance than a coil having fewer turns.

Frequency plays a role in induction also. If the frequency of AC is low, the current will have more time to reach maximum before the polarity is reversed. The higher the frequency, the lower the current through the circuit. Frequency affects the opposition to current flow as well as circuit induction.

Pure inductance uses no power, the electrical energy that is taken is returned directly to the circuit as electrical energy, whereas the electrical energy taken in a resistance is converted into heat and cannot be returned to the circuit. Inductance uses electrical energy to create a magnetic field and the magnetic field restores the energy to the line when it collapes. That's why in an AC circuit volts times amps = volt-amps not watts. In an AC circuit, voltage times amps has little to do with actual power consumed, since no power (watts) is consumed in a pure inductive or capacitive AC circuit. In AC, this is called volt-amps, **wattless** power.

The picture to the left shows the relationship of induction to water. When a garden hose is wrapped around a post several times the coiling will oppose the normal flow of water to slow it down. A plumber refers to this as back pressure, like a restriction to the flow.
  Electrically it offers a resistance to the normal flow of current. We call it inductance.

Some electricians may not know the difference that AC makes in a circuit compared to DC, but the circuit knows the difference.

Inductive reactance is measured in ohms just as resistance is. The symbol letter for inductance is "L".

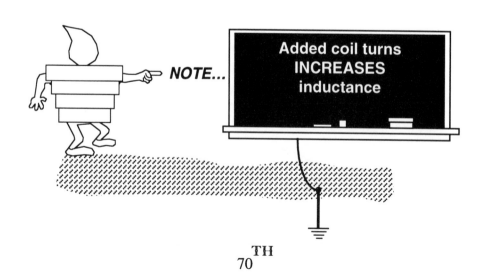

NOTE...

Added coil turns
INCREASES
inductance

The other component of an AC circuit is **capacitive** reactance; current that starts out high and drops after the insulation has been charged to full voltage.

Capacitance opposes any change in circuit voltage. When the voltage increases, capacitance tries to hold it down. When voltage decreases, capacitance tries to hold it up.

Capacitance affects DC circuits only when turned on and off. In AC circuits the voltage is changing 60 times a second so the effect of capacitance is **continuous**. The capacitance may be so small that its effect on the circuit is negligible.

A capacitor (sometimes called a condenser) exists whenever an insulating material separates two conductors that have a voltage difference between them. Capacitors are installed into a circuit to **deliberately** add capacitance to the circuit.

Capacitive reactance can be from the location and arrangement of electrical equipment in the circuit. Capacitance is often built into the circuit when insulated conductors are installed in a metal conduit.

The amount of capacitance present in a circuit depends on the physical construction of the circuit and the electrical devices used.

Capacitance related to water is like the water flow in a garden hose when you first turn on the valve; the water starts out fast and drops after the hose is filled. Electrically, the current starts out high and drops after the insulation has been charged to full voltage.

Capacitive reactance is also measured in ohms. The symbol letter for capacitance is "C".

Impedance is the **total opposition** to the flow of current in an **AC** circuit. To calculate the total opposition it is necessary to add the resistance, the inductive reactance, and the capacitive reactance: all three factors measured in **ohms**.

The symbol letter for impedance is "Z".

Reactance of an AC circuit is mainly determined by the **spacing** between conductors. Reactance is only slightly affected by conductor size. Circuit resistance is affected by conductor size. If the conductors are as close together as possible, the impedance caused by induction will be as low as possible.

When a conductor carries a current, it sets up a magnetic field around the conductor. This is called self-induction. When installing two conductors in the same metal raceway, the current is traveling in two different directions, the magnetic fields of the two currents flowing in opposite directions actually cancel each other out to keep induction at a minimum. This is the reason the Code requires keeping conductors grouped together in metal conduits. Phase conductors, and where used, the neutral and equipment grounding conductor shall be grouped together to avoid heating the surrounding metal conduit by induction.

 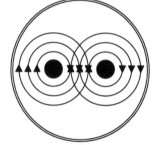

MAGNETIC FIELD

The Code even further states that all conductors of the same circuit and, where used, the neutral and all equipment grounding conductors shall be installed in the same raceway or close together in the **same trench**. Conductors in parallel installed in raceways shall be permitted, but each raceway shall contain **all conductors of the same circuit including grounding conductors**.

The strength of the magnetic field depends on the amount of current flow. If the conductor is straight, there will be little self-induction, but if coiled the magnetic effect is greater.

Added coil turns increase the inductance

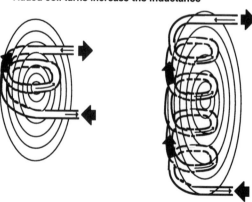

If the surrounding medium is air the self-induction will be smaller, but if the conductor is surrounded by iron, the self-induction is considerably higher. The noninductive coil has a wire doubled back, the magnetic fields will cancel and the inductance will be zero.

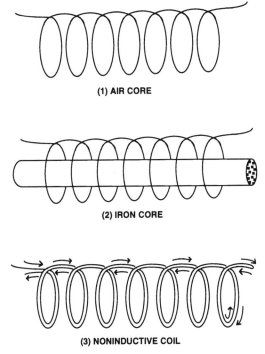

(1) AIR CORE

(2) IRON CORE

(3) NONINDUCTIVE COIL

Reactance in a 40 amp or less circuit is significant. In circuits of 100-200 amperes reactance may be a prominent element whereas reactance is the the predominant element for circuits over **200 amperes**.

HARMONICS

AC is delivered to the customers by the utility company for powering loads such as lighting, heating and motors. However, electronic equipment such as computers, solid-state drives, data processing equipment, etc. require DC power. As a result, the AC must be converted to DC where electronic equipment is supplied.

The process of converting AC to DC is done by the power supply which is located in the electronic equipment itself. Because the power supply does not draw current in direct proportion to the voltage, it is referred to as a **non-linear** load.

Examples of linear loads are incandescent lighting, resistive heating and motors. These loads are exempt from harmonic currents.

Examples of **non-linear** loads which contain harmonics are computers, static power converters used in adjustable speed drives, solid-state frequency converters, uninterruptible power supplies (UPS), electric welders, discharge lighting, etc.

 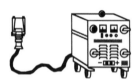  

When a linear load is turned on, the voltage and current start and turn off together. When a non-linear load is turned on, the voltage starts but the current is purposely delayed.

Harmonic simply indicates that the current waveform is distorted. The closer the waveform is to a fundamental sine wave, the lower the harmonic content. With a fundamental sine wave, there are no high order harmonics.

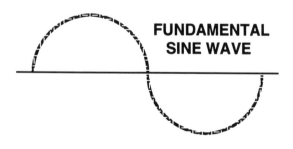

FUNDAMENTAL SINE WAVE

3rd HARMONIC WAVE FORM

A 3rd harmonic makes 3 alternations in one alternation of the fundamental wave form. A 5th harmonic makes 5 alternations in one alternation of the fundamental wave. The 7th harmonic makes 7 alternations, and so on.

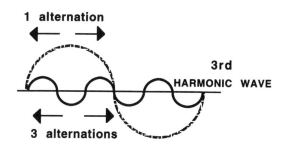

The highest peak of the wave is determined by **adding** all of the odd harmonics together. The frequency is determined by the number of complete cycles per second, measured in Hertz. 60 cycles per second equals 60 Hertz, or 60 Hz.

On a 60 Hz AC system the 3rd harmonic is 180 Hz, the 5th harmonic is 300 Hz, the 7th harmonic is 420 Hz, etc.

HARMONICS ARE ADDITIVE

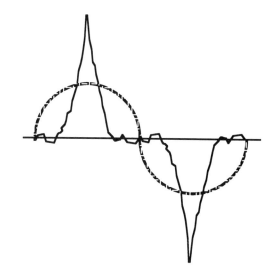

A **harmonic wave** is a **distorted wave** pattern consisting of the fundamental wave and other **higher frequency waves** that are superimposed on the fundamental wave.

The harmonic currents are delayed then **added** together and then burst into action causing a high peak wave form and a higher frequency.

Heat is increased by an increase in current frequency. The heating effect on transformers, circuit breakers and conductors supplying **non-linear** loads is a function of **I²R**.

The higher I²R heating where harmonic currents are supplied is caused by what is known as **skin effect**. Skin effect is an increase in resistance due to the fact that **higher-frequency** currents flow on the **skin** of the conductor, rather than throughout the entire conductor.

AC tends to flow along the surface of a conductor. DC acts through the entire cross-sectional area of the conductor in a uniform manner. The name skin effect is given to the action whereby AC is forced toward the surface of the conductor. Because of skin effect, there is less useful copper conductive area with AC. As a result, there is an increase in resistance.

CROSS-SECTIONAL AREA DENSITY

DC   AC

For the 3rd harmonic, instead of 60 Hz it's now 180 Hz, there is a 42% change in the skin effect concentration point. For the 5th harmonic there is a 55% difference and a 62% difference for the 7th harmonic. The result is a proportionate increase of resistance.

As you can see, the harmonic currents raised the frequency, thus raising the resistance and the I²R heating effect.

In multiwire branch circuits, the odd numbered harmonics do not cancel out on the neutral, but are additive, resulting in a high neutral load. Because the heating effect on the conductor is proportional to I²R and because the conductor resistance will be greater at 180 Hz than at 60 Hz, the heating effect in the neutral conductor will be greater than that of the phase conductors.

This is the reason in Note 10a of Table 310-16 of the Code it requires counting the neutral conductor in a 3ø, 4-wire circuit supplying **electric discharge lighting**. The neutral conductor is actually **hotter** in temperature than the phase conductors.

An electrician is familar with the fluorescent light fixture containing a ballast. This fixture is referred to as discharge lighting since it contains a ballast (winding).

Harmonics cause problems to transformers and neutral conductors in multiwire feeders and branch circuits. The largest contributor to harmonic distortion is the static power converter used in adjustable speed drives.

One of the components for which there is great concern is the the neutral conductor in a multiwire branch circuit. There will be no current flow on the circuit neutral conductor if the circuit supplies the same amount of **resistive** loads from each phase to neutral. But, with three single-phase **non-linear** loads fed from a 208/120v three-phase feeder due to the phase relationship there is **no** cancellation of the harmonic currents in the neutral conductor.

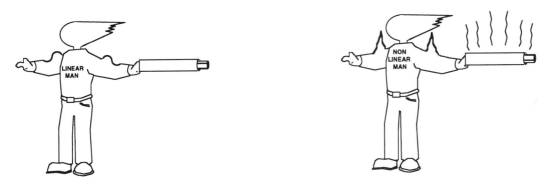

Instead, the neutral will carry the current drawn by each phase, and where more than one such load is fed from a given phase, the current drawn by each load on that phase will **add** in the neutral. The heating effect (rms current value) on the neutral could be equal to 1.732 times the current of one phase.

By using a **separate neutral** for each branch circuit phase conductor you could eliminate the **effect** of harmonic loading on the **single** neutral conductor of a multiwire branch circuit. This would not eliminate the harmonics. There would still be harmonic currents in the feeder conductors, which will be carried by the transformer.

Transformers are overheating and burning up and don't appear to be overloaded. Standard dry-type transformers were never designed to handle the harmonic currents that cause added heating. Heat determines the life of the insulation.

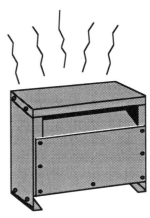

Transformers are now available to handle the harmonic currents. These transformers are **K-Factor rated**. The conventional dry-type transformer has a K-Factor of one. Today with the non-linear loading, a **minimum** K-Factor of 4 is recommended for minimum design.

K-Factor K4 means the transformer is built to handle 4 times the eddy current loss and will allow the transformer to operate within the temperature limit with these harmonic currents.

The K-Factor transformer cost more than the conventional dry-type, but the cost of the total installation is less. A conventional K1 transformer would require a much larger kva rating thus requiring larger conductors, equipment, circuit breakers, etc. As an electrical designer we must remember we have **long term** obligations.

The transformer must be "K-Factor" rated for harmonic loading or they must be derated in kva to assure that the rated-temperature rise is not exceeded.

K-Factor rated transformers do **not** get rid of the harmonic currents, they are designed to handle the extra heat generated by these currents. Nobody even proposes that it is advisable to try to get rid of the harmonic currents.

In many cases harmonic currents are an invisable problem for the electrician. A non-rms amp clamp meter shows the transformer is only **half loaded,** but the transformer feels **really hot**. You should trust the heat and not the meter.

Average-rms ammeters are **not** reliable instruments for evaluating an electrical system's harmonic content. For accurate indication of an electrical system's content, use only a **true-rms meter**.

Phase conductors have been measured showing a balanced load 125 amps per phase and the **neutral** showing **155 amps**. Now you can see how the neutral becomes **a current-carrying conductor** with the added harmonic current heat.

It is quite apparent that feeders and branch circuits serving the **average office space** can have **greater** currents in the neutral than the phase conductors as a result of these **additive** harmonics.

The estimate is that the 1990 load on the utility is 15% harmonic and by the year 2000 harmonic currents will constitute 50% of the loading on the utility transformer.

This message on harmonic currents needs to reach the electrician so the electrician fully understands this problem in our industry. It has been estimated that 70% of the electrical designing is done by the electrician and electrical contractor.

Remember, conductor sizing from the Code is based on **60 Hz**. The system must be designed for the extra heat produced by these non-linear loads.

One might consider the use of nonferrous raceways such as aluminum or PVC. This is a standard practice in 400 Hz applications such as aircraft and large computer rooms to reduce heating (eddy currents - skin effect) from the adjacent steel raceways. Remember, 400 Hz is very nearly the 7th harmonic of a 60 Hz system.

Higher harmonics are worse, percentage wise, than the lower 3rd harmonic.

An electrician can not calculate the amount or order of harmonics contained in a piece of equipment. A ballast generally contains 3rd harmonics, but another type of ballast may contain even a higher order of harmonic. A computer may have some 5th, 7th, 9th or even higher harmonics with different percentages of each order of harmonics.

There is no perfect way, at this writing, to solve this **cancer** that is eating away at our conductors and transformers.

When computers, data processing equipment and solid state devices are involved in the circuitry, the electrician should consider the K-Factor transformer, derating the kva of an existing transformer, upsizing the conductors, installing separate or oversized neutrals on multiwire circuits.

On a 20 amp receptacle multiwire branch circuit supplying computers, it is recommended to use #12 ungrounded (hot) circuit conductors with a **#8** (white) grounded or neutral conductor.

Cable manufacturers are now making a cable containing #12 circuit conductors with a **#8 "super neutral"** conductor. Cables with a individual neutral per phase conductor are also available.

An oversized neutral is not necessary to accommodate the harmonics generated by the 3rd harmonic in ballasts.

Definition: A neutral conductor carries only the **unbalanced** current of a circuit, as the neutral conductor of a 3-wire single-phase circuit or a 4-wire three-phase circuit.

The Edison 3-wire system involves connecting two 120 volt supplies in **series** in a way that their polarities cause the voltages to be added. The common point is called the **neutral**.

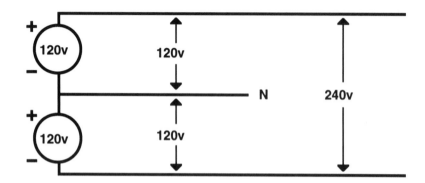

In a 2-wire, 120v circuit, the grounded conductor (identified white in color) is **NOT** a neutral conductor. In a 2-wire circuit the grounded conductor carries the same amount of current as the ungrounded (hot) conductor carries. •Remember the definition of a neutral, it carries the **unbalanced current**. You must have a 3-wire circuit to have a **neutral** conductor.

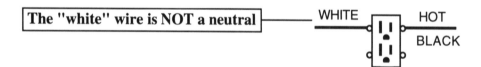

The "white" wire is NOT a neutral

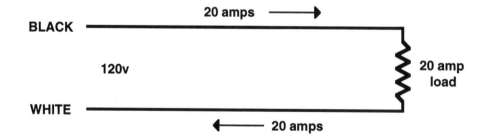

The next sketch shows two 20 amp, 120 volt loads connected, using four conductors. The grounded (white) conductors connect together at the neutral bar in the load center.

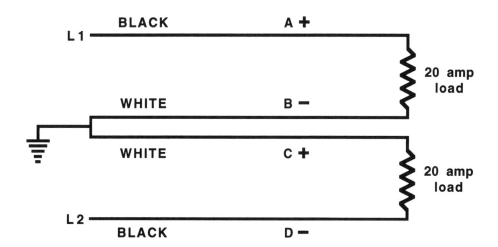

Why use two grounded (white) conductors? Why not use just one? You may think that by using **one** white conductor to serve two 20 amp loads, the **one** white conductor would have to be sized **twice** as large to carry 40 amps. This is an incorrect conclusion.

The next sketch shows the same 20 amp loads using only 3 wires, utilizing the neutral conductor.

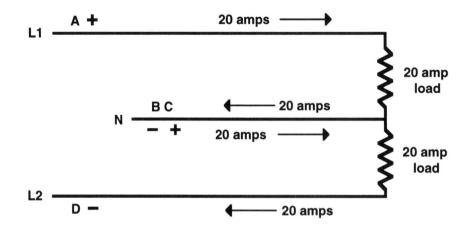

Each of the conductors B and C carries 20 amps, but note the direction of the arrows. The flow of current in conductor B at any **instant** is in an **opposite** direction of conductor C. So at any given instant, the single neutral conductor is said to be carrying 20 amps in one direction and 20 amps in the **opposite direction**, the two cancel each other and the flow of current in the neutral conductor is zero.

The system is actually 240 volts with the two 20 amp 120 volt loads in **series**.

Since the loads have equal resistance, the voltage of 240 would divide, 120 volts to each load. This is a **balanced** system. In a balanced system the neutral conductor carries zero current.

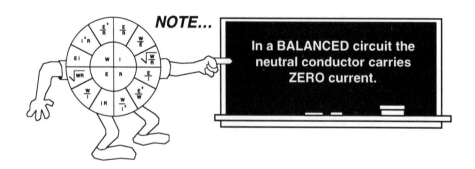

The next sketch shows an **unbalanced** system and the effect it has on the neutral conductor.

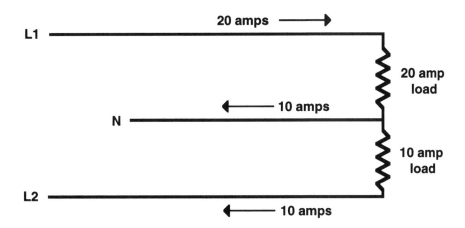

The neutral conductor carries the **unbalanced** current, 10 amps. The **maximum** current the neutral conductor would ever carry in this sketch would be 20 amps. If the 10 amp load on line 2 was shut off, the neutral conductor would have to carry the 20 amp load from line 1. The maximum neutral current would be 20.

A loose neutral connection will cause unusual things to happen in a circuit, fan motors change speed, lights flicker, etc.

A loose neutral connection is a good place for a serviceman to start looking when experiencing unusual happenings in a circuit.

The next sketch shows an open neutral conductor in the system.

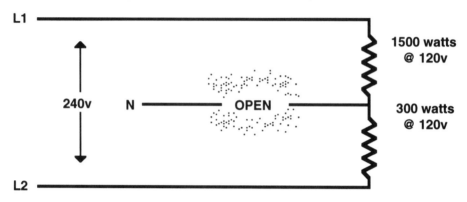

With an open neutral conductor this becomes a 240 volt **series** circuit.

Example: Find the total resistance in this series circuit.

Solution: The 1500 watt load is rated @ 120v, its resistance is fixed and cannot change. Use Ohm's Law formula $R = E^2/W = 120v \times 120v/1500w = 9.6$ ohms.

The 300 watt load is rated @ 120v, its resistance is fixed and cannot change. $R = E^2/W = 120v \times 120v/300w = 48$ ohms.

R total = R1 + R2   9.6 ohms + 48 ohms = **57.6 ohms total series resistance.**

Example: Find the current flowing in this series circuit.

Solution: Use Ohm's Law formula $I = E/R = 240v/57.6\Omega = 4.1666$ or **4.17 amps flowing**.

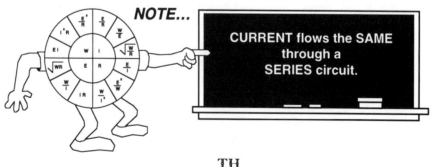

NOTE...

CURRENT flows the SAME through a SERIES circuit.

Example: Find the voltage across the 1500 watt load.

Solution: Use Ohm's Law formula $E = I \times R = 4.17$ amps x 9.6 ohms = **40 volts** (across the 1500 watt load).

Example: Find the voltage across the 300 watt load.

Solution: Use Ohm's Law formula $E = I \times R = 4.17$ amps x 48 ohms = **200 volts** (across the 300 watt load).

•Checkpoint: 40 volts + 200 volts = 240 volts (the applied voltage).

   You can see the danger involved with an **open neutral** conductor. The 1500 watt load rated at 120 volts would receive only **40 volts** which would not damage any lighting or heating equipment, but a motor would not operate properly.

   The 300 watt load rated at 120 volts would receive **200 volts**. This higher voltage will damage 120 volt rated equipment.

NOTE...

Never FUSE the neutral conductor, nor depend on a device for continuity.

The neutral conductor is common to both circuits. Extreme caution must be used when connecting a three-wire branch circuit to the load panel. The **black** and **red** conductors of the three-wire cable must be connected to **OPPOSITE** lines in the panel to prevent heavy overloading of the neutral conductor.

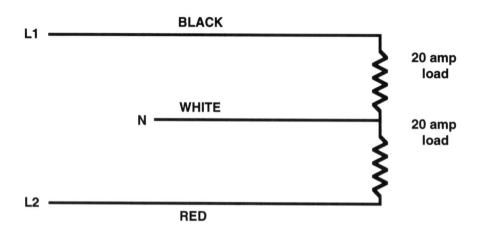

Connect the black conductor to circuit #5 in the panel which is line 1. Connect the red conductor to circuit #7 which is line 2. Properly connected and with both loads "on", the neutral conductor would carry zero current. The maximum current the neutral would carry is 20 amps if either load was shut off.

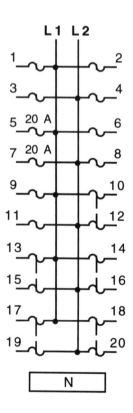

The three-wire branch circuit connected **incorrectly**.

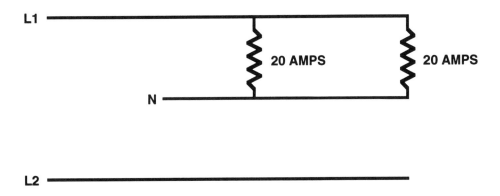

If both the black and red wires were connected to the **same** line in the panel with both 20 amp loads "on", the white wire would carry 40 amps which is an overload on a #12 conductor.

This is referred to as the "white" wire rather than the neutral. By connecting both loads to the same line in a three-wire circuit you no longer have a neutral. Remember the definition of a neutral; it carries only the unbalanced current.

A multiwire branch circuit has two ungrounded conductors with a potential difference between them.

•Checkpoint: The neutral conductor in a three-wire branch circuit shall not be dependent on device connections, such as receptacles, where the removal of the device would interrupt the continuity of the neutral conductor. A pigtail is required.

THE SPLIT-WIRE BRANCH CIRCUIT

This is a circuit where the top portion of the duplex receptacle is hot all the time, while the bottom portion of the duplex receptacle is controlled by a wall switch.

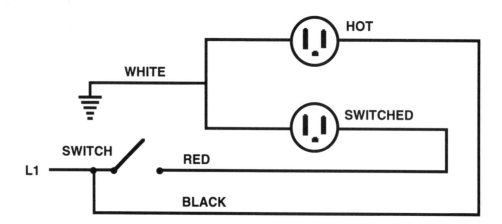

When connecting the split-wire or two-wire branch circuit, **both** the red and black wires are connected to the **same** line either L1 or L2. The white wire is **not** a neutral conductor.

NOTE...

Don't confuse the split-wire with the three-wire circuit.

MATH REVIEW FOR THE EXAM

This section will help you **relearn** mathematical fundamentals. The basic math is not covered in the following pages, only the math as applied to the electrical exam.

Your **calculator** is a very important item that you need to practice and become familiar with. A calculator can reduce the time involved in solving a calculation question and can also provide accuracy. But remember, the **right** numbers have to be pressed to get the **right** answer. It would be a good idea the day of the exam to take along a **spare** calculator as a back up, just in case you would experience problems with your other calculator.

During the exam as you apply Ohm's Law formulas and math you need to **understand what you read**.

When two or more numbers or letters, each in parentheses, follow each other, they are to be **multiplied**.

Example: (2) (4) (6)   This means 2 x 4 x 6 = 48

Example: 2KDI means (2) (K) (D) (I)   This means 2 x K x D x I

Example: va means (v) (a)   This means v x a

Example: (2) (4) -2 This means 2 x 4 = 8 - 2 = 6

Example: (2) (4-2)   This means, work subtraction first and then multiply 4 - 2 = 2 x 2 = 4

Example: (2) (4 + 2) This means, work addition first and then multiply 4 + 2 = 6 x 2 = 12

NOTE...

Always have a SPARE calculator available as a back up.

When **square root** is to be extracted, as indicated by the sign $\sqrt{}$, everything under the sign must be done first, then the square root extracted.

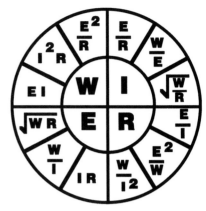

Example: Ohm's Law circle shows: $E = \sqrt{WR}$

 $W = 100$ watts $R = 144$ ohms

First multiply 100 watts by 144 ohms = 14,400. Now press the $\sqrt{}$ button on your calculator, answer = **120 volts**. 120 is the square root of 14,400. 120 x 120 = 14,400.

Example: The Ohm's Law circle shows: $I = \sqrt{W/R}$ $W = 100$ watts $R = 144$ ohms

First divide 100 watts by 144 ohms = .6944444. Now press the $\sqrt{}$ button on your calculator, answer = **0.8333333** or **0.83 amps**.

Example: Formula for impedance: $Z = \sqrt{R^2 + X^2}$ $R = 10$ ohms $X = 15$ ohms

First multiply 10 x 10 = 100. Then multiply 15 x 15 = 225. Now add 100 + 225 = 325. Now press the $\sqrt{}$ button, answer = **18**.

Where a number is followed by a second number that is placed just above and to the right of the first number (10^2), the second number (^{2}) is called an **exponent**. It means the first number is to be used as a factor in **multiplication**, as often as indicated by the exponent.

Example: Ohm's Law circle shows $W = I^2R$

$I = 10$ amp $R = 15$ ohm

This means $10 \times 10 \times 15 = $ **1500 watts**.

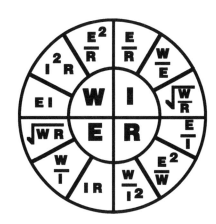

Example: Ohm's Law circle shows $R = W/I^2$

$W = 1500$ watts $I = 10$ amps

This means $\dfrac{1500}{10 \times 10}$ or $\dfrac{1500}{100} = $ **15 ohms**.

Example: 4^2 means 4 "to the second power" or 4 square, $4 \times 4 = $ **16**

Example: 4^3 means $4 \times 4 \times 4 = $ **64**

Example: 5^4 means $5 \times 5 \times 5 \times 5 = $ **625**

As you can see by now, you must first **understand** how a formula is written before you can accurately apply it.

Example: A formula to find **distance** in a voltage drop calculation $D = \dfrac{CM \times VD}{2 \times K \times I}$

$CM = 10380$ $VD = 3.6$ $K = 12.9$ $I = 10$

$D = \dfrac{10380 \times 3.6}{2 \times 12.9 \times 10}$

This formula means $10380 \times 3.6 = 37,368$ divided by $(2 \times 12.9 \times 10) = 258$.

$37,369/258 = $ **144.8 feet distance**.

A simple way to work this calculation for distance, using your calculator, would be:
First clear your calculator to 0.
Now **press** 10380, **press** X, **press** 3.6
Now **press** divide, **press** 2, **press** divide, **press** 12.9, **press** divide, **press** 10. Now **press** =, your calculator should read **144.8372**.

Work this drill a few times and see how easy it becomes!

Some formulas can be made easier to understand. The following is an example of a master electrician exam question.

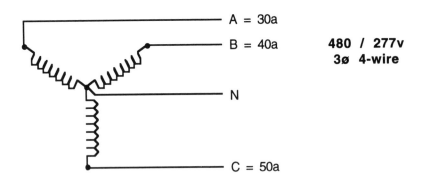

A = 30a
B = 40a

480 / 277v
3ø 4-wire

N

C = 50a

Three loads are connected line to neutral, with all loads **"on"**, what is the unbalanced current the neutral conductor is carrying?

At first, the formula looks very difficult, but it's not.

$$In = \sqrt{I^2A + I^2B + I^2C - (IA\ IB) - (IB\ IC) - (IC\ IA)}$$

Remember that everything **under** the square root sign must be done first, which means:

current in A squared = 30 x 30 = 900
+current in B squared = 40 x 40 = 1600
+current in C squared = 50 x 50 = 2500
                                 5000 total (call this total X)

The right side of the formula shows:

current in A x current in B = 30 x 40 = 1200
current in B x current in C = 40 x 50 = 2000
current in C x current in A = 50 x 30 = 1500
                                       4700 total (call this total Y)

Substract total Y from total X: 5000 (total X)
                                 -4700 (total Y)
                                   300

Extract the square root by **pressing** the $\sqrt{}$ button on your calculator. The answer is **17.32 amps**, the unbalanced current flowing in the neutral.

17.320508 is the square root of 300; 17.320508 x 17.320508 = 300.

TEMPERATURE CONVERSION CELSIUS-FAHRENHEIT FORMULAS

	CELSIUS	FAHRENHEIT
Water boils at	100°	212°
Water freezes at	0°	32°
Difference	100°	180°

The change in Celsius is equivalent to 180/100 or 9/5 or 1.8° change on the Fahrenheit scale. A degree of change on the Fahrenheit scale is equivalent to 100/180 or 5/9 or .555° change on the Celsius scale.

The conversion formulas are:

(degrees F -32) (5/9) = degrees Celsius
(degrees C) (9/5) + 32 = degrees Fahrenheit

As an electrician we are familiar with NEC Table 310-16 Ampacity which shows a correction factor for conductor ampacities when the ambient temperature exceeds 86°F or 30°C.

Let's apply the formulas to these temperatures:

The formula shows that the first step is to subtract 32° from 86°= 54°. Now multiply 54° by 5/9 = 270/9 = **30°C**.

Example: Convert 30°C to 86°F

The formula shows that the first step is to multiply 30°C x 9/5 = 270/5 = 54

54 + 32 = **86°F**.

PERCENTAGE and DECIMAL POINT

DECIMAL POINT

.3   reads "three tenths"
.03   reads "three hundredths"
.003 reads "three thousandths"

PERCENTAGE

Percentage is used to indicate a number of parts of **one hundred**. One percent (1%) of a quantity means 1/100 (fraction form) or .01 (decimal form).

To change a decimal to a percent, move the decimal point two places to the **right** and add the % sign.

Example: 2.50 = 250%, 1.25 = 125%, .80 = 80%, .70 = 70%, .40 = 40%, .03 = 3%

Percents may be changed to decimals by moving the decimal point two places to the **left** and dropping the % sign.

Example: 250% = 2.50, 125% = 1.25, 80% = .80, 70% = .70, 40% = .40, 3% = .03

Applying percentages to exam calculations: To find the full-load current of a 208 volt single-phase motor you **increase** the 230 volt full-load current 10%.

Example: 230 volt full-load current from Table 430-148 = 28 amps x 10% = 2.8 amps, to **increase** you add 28 amps + 2.8 amps = **30.8 amps**.

To eliminate the last step of addition, multiply 28 amps x 110% = 30.8, or multiply 28 amps x 1.10 = 30.8. It would be the same as saying: If you had 100 cement blocks and you increased them 10%, how many would you have?

10% of 100 = 10   100 blocks + 10 = 110 blocks or 100 x 1.10 = 110 blocks.

Most exams require 75% to pass the exam, if you had 120 questions on the exam, how many correct would you have to have to score 75%?

Solution: 120 questions x 75% = **90 correct**.

If you had a total of 120 questions on the exam and 75 were correct, what would your score be?

Solution: 75/120 = .625 or **62.5%**

PREFIX	ABBREVIATION	MEANING	MATH EQUIVALENT
kilo	k	one thousand times	10^3
milli	m	one thousandth part of	10^{-3}
mega	M	one million times	10^6
micro	u	one millionth part of	10^{-6}

Example: A thousandth (1/1000) of a volt = millivolt
 A million watts (1,000,000) = megawatt
 One kilowatt = 1,000 watts
 10 megohms = 10 million ohms

In measurement conversion, the exponent tells you how the decimal point should be moved:

1) To change from any unit of measurement to a **larger** one, move the decimal point to the **left** by the number of places equal to the difference between their exponents.

Example: Convert 240 volts to kilovolts.

Solution: kilo = 10^3 move the decimal point 3 places to the left = **.240 kilovolts**.

Example: Convert 450 va to kilo-volt-amps (kva).

Solution: kilo = 10^3 move the decimal point 3 places to the left = **.450 kva**.

Example: Convert 150,000 ohms to megohms.

Solution: mega = 10^6 move the decimal point 6 places to the left = **.15 megohm**.

Example: Convert 250,000 cm to kcmil.

Solution: m = 10^3 move the decimal point 3 places to the left = **250 kcmil**.

2) To change from any unit of measure to a **smaller** one, move the decimal point to the **right** by the number of places equal to the difference between their exponents.

Example: Convert 8.4 kw to watts.

Solution: m = 10^3 move the decimal point 3 places to the right = **8400 watts**.

Example: Convert 1000 kcmil to cm.

Solution: m = 10^3 move the decimal 3 places to the right = **1,000,000 cm**.

Exam question:

   The resistance for a thousand feet of conductor is 0.0967 ohms. What is the resistance for 471 feet of this conductor?

Solution: 0.0967Ω per m/ft/1000 feet = 0.0000967 ohms resistance per foot. Now multiply 0.0000967 ohms x 471 feet = **0.0455457**. An easier way to work this calculation and eliminate a step is to multiply 0.0967Ω x .471 feet = **0.0455457Ω**. Since the calculation is based on a thousand feet, move the decimal point 3 places for a thousand. 471 feet = .471 feet.

Exam Question:

What are the circular mils of a 1/4" x 1" bus bar?

Solution: thickness x width = area   thickness = 1/4" = .25" x 1000 = 250 mils
width = 1" x 1000 = 1000 mils   250 mils x 1000 mils = 250,000 square mils
   To convert square mils to circular mils, multiply by 1.272.
250,000 square mils x 1.272 = **318,000 circular mils**.

INTERPOLATION

Exam question: What is the full-load current of a 4 hp 230 volt
                single-phase motor?

Solution: NEC 430-6. Use the values given in Table 430-148, **interpolated** if necessary.

Table 430-148   3 hp = 17 amps
                5 hp = 28 amps

   The **difference** in hp between 3 hp and 5 hp = 2 hp
   The **difference** in amps between 17 amps and 28 amps = 11 amps
   divide 11 by 2 = 5.5 amps
   3 hp = 17 amps + 5.5 amps = **22.5 amp full-load current** for a 4 hp motor interpolated.

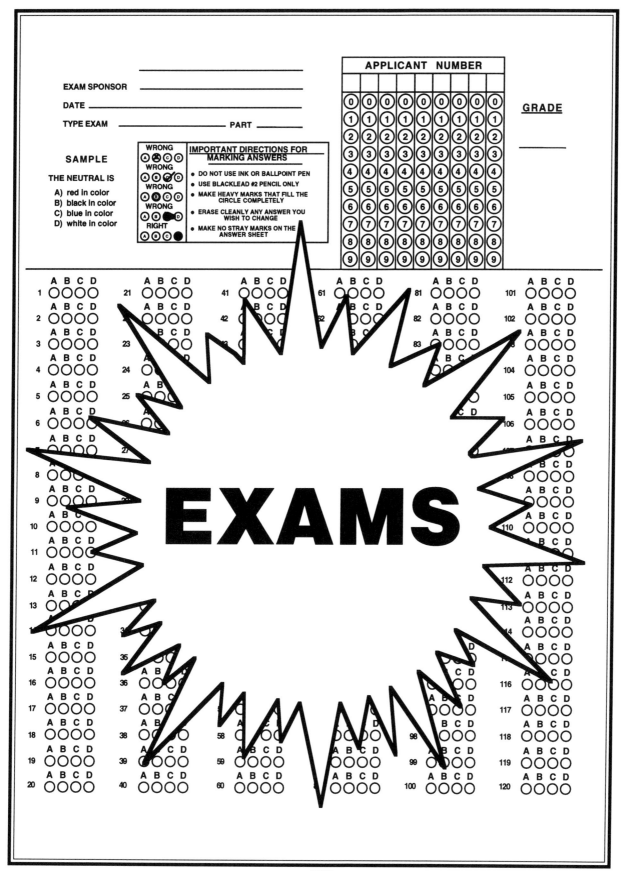

1. Electrons flowing in a conductor will always create a(an) ____.

(a) friction   (b) fluorescence   (c) magnetic field   (d) ultraviolet light

2. AC voltages may be increased or decreased by a ____.

(a) rectifier   (b) motor   (c) transformer   (d) shunt

3. The number of watts of heat given off by a resistor are expressed by the formula I^2R. If 10 volts are applied to a 5 ohm resistor, the heat given off will be ____ watts.

(a) 500   (b) 250   (c) 50   (d) 20

4. What percentage of the peak voltage is the effective voltage?

(a) 68.9%   (b) 69.6%   (c) 70.7%   (d) 71.1%

5. For a given line voltage, four heater coils will consume the most power when connected ____.

(a) all in series
(b) all in parallel
(c) with 2 parallel pairs in series
(d) 1 pair in parallel with the other two in series

6. Electricity can be produced from ____ different ways.

(a) eight   (b) six   (c) ten   (d) twelve

7. A ____ is a device that transforms chemical energy into electrical energy.

(a) thermocouple   (b) electron   (c) cell   (d) hydrometer

1. To reduce DC voltages you would use a(an) ____.

(a) resistor   (b) transformer   (c) balancer set   (d) inverter

2. ____ is the ability of a material to permit the flow of electrons.

(a) Voltage   (b) Current   (c) Resistance   (d) Conductance

3. The instrument which is used to measure electric current is a(an) ____.

(a) wattmeter   (b) ohmmeter   (c) ammeter   (d) voltmeter

4. Which one of the following statements is **false?**

(a) The electrolyte can be in liquid form or a paste
(b) Primary batteries are mostly used where limited current is required
(c) An automotive battery is a good example of a primary battery
(d) The electron theory is that current flows from negative to positive

5. When the current leads the voltage, what type of circuit is it?

(a) in phase   (b) inductive   (c) capacitive   (d) all of these

6. The neutral must not be broken at receptacles ____.

(a) on 2-wire circuits
(b) not having a grounded conductor
(c) on multi-wire circuits
(d) having a, b or c

7. The advantage of AC over DC includes which of the following?

(a) better speed control   (b) ease of voltage variation
(c) lower resistance at high currents   (d) impedance is greater

1. Electrodes are usually made of strips of ____.

(a) copper & zinc (b) silver & lead (c) lead & tin (d) tin & copper

2. The ____ is the angle between the real power and the apparent power.

(a) lag angle (b) power factor angle (c) va angle (d) watt angle

3. Which one of the following statements is **false?**

(a) Water has a specific gravity of 1.000
(b) Most storage batteries use 80° F as a normal temperature to read specific gravity
(c) When water is added to a battery, it should be charged for at least one hour before a reading is taken
(d) All liquids have the same density

4. A magnet is normally made of ____.

(a) stainless steel (b) iron (c) lead (d) copper

5. The voltage loss across a portion of a circuit is called ____.

(a) power factor (b) I²R loss (c) voltage drop (d) none of these

6. Which of the following is a **true** statement?

(a) In the early days of electricity only AC was available
(b) AC generators can be built with much larger power than DC
(c) DC voltages are usually stepped up or down with a transformer
(d) AC voltages are usually stepped up or down with a rectifier

7. A kva is equal to ____.

(a) 100 va (b) 1000 v (c) 1000 w (d) 1000 va

1. In a series circuit _____ is common.

(a) voltage   (b) wattage   (c) current   (d) resistance

2. Three 9 ohm resistors connected in parallel have a total resistance of _____ ohms.

(a) 27   (b) 9   (c) 3   (d) none of these

3. When a current leaves its intended path and returns to the source, bypassing the load, the circuit is _____.

(a) open   (b) shorted   (c) incomplete   (d) broken

4. Ohm's Law is _____.

(a) an equation for determining power
(b) a measurement of the I²R losses
(c) the relationship between voltage, current and power
(d) the relationship between voltage, current and resistance

5. Electrical pressure is measured in _____.

(a) coulombs   (b) amperes   (c) watts   (d) volts

6. Which of the following converts mechanical energy into electrical energy?

(a) fan   (b) motor   (c) generator   (d) battery

7. A thermocouple will transform _____ into electricity.

(a) current   (b) heat   (c) work   (d) watts

EXAM 5 QUESTIONS

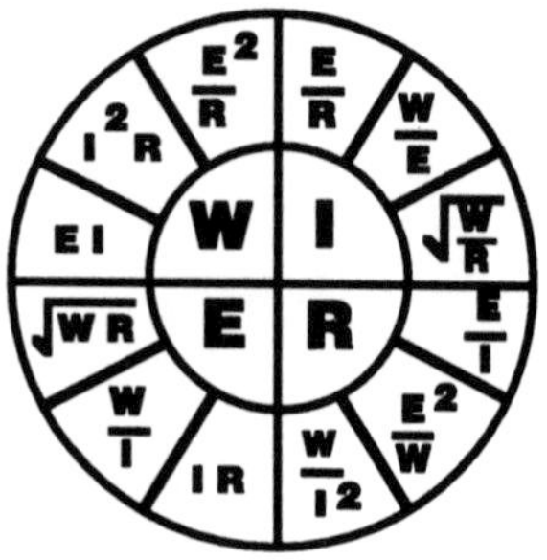

1. A rectifier is used to ____.

(a) change DC to AC (b) limit current
(c) change AC to DC (d) both b and C

2. Capacitance is measured in ____.

(a) ohms (b) volts (c) farads (d) henrys

3. Capacitive reactance is measured in _____.

(a) ohms (b) henrys (c) resonance (d) impedance

4. Storage batteries are rated in ____.

(a) volt-amps (b) watt-hours (c) volt-hours (d) amp-hours

5. It is customary to speak of the electromotive force as the ____ of the circuit.

(a) current (b) voltage (c) wattage (d) resistance

6. A 20 amp fuse will blow when a load of ____ watts is connected to it. (115 volt source)

(a) 1500 (b) 2000 (c) 2500 (d) none of these

7. Electricity produced by means of pressure to a material is called ____.

(a) thermoelectricity
(b) piezoelectricity
(c) electrochemistry
(d) photoconduction

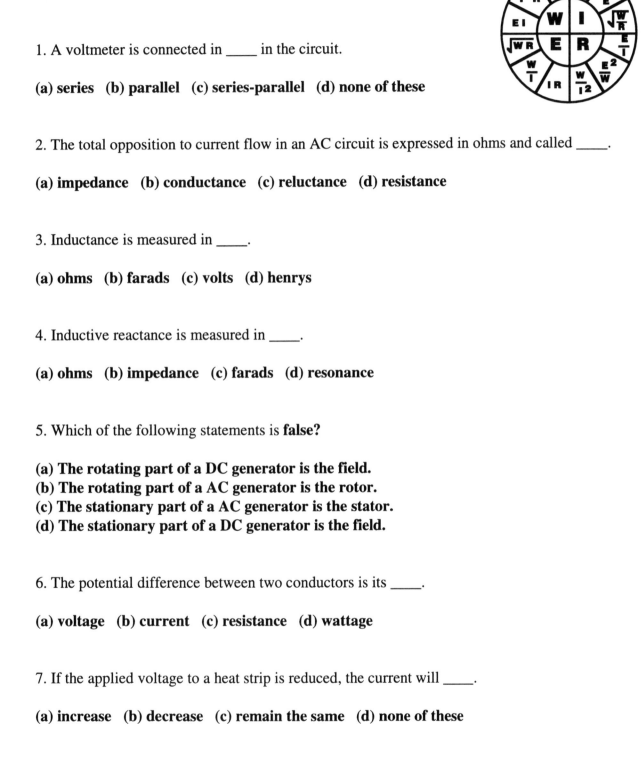

EXAM 6 QUESTIONS

1. A voltmeter is connected in _____ in the circuit.

(a) series   (b) parallel   (c) series-parallel   (d) none of these

2. The total opposition to current flow in an AC circuit is expressed in ohms and called _____.

(a) impedance   (b) conductance   (c) reluctance   (d) resistance

3. Inductance is measured in _____.

(a) ohms   (b) farads   (c) volts   (d) henrys

4. Inductive reactance is measured in _____.

(a) ohms   (b) impedance   (c) farads   (d) resonance

5. Which of the following statements is **false?**

(a) The rotating part of a DC generator is the field.
(b) The rotating part of a AC generator is the rotor.
(c) The stationary part of a AC generator is the stator.
(d) The stationary part of a DC generator is the field.

6. The potential difference between two conductors is its _____.

(a) voltage   (b) current   (c) resistance   (d) wattage

7. If the applied voltage to a heat strip is reduced, the current will _____.

(a) increase   (b) decrease   (c) remain the same   (d) none of these

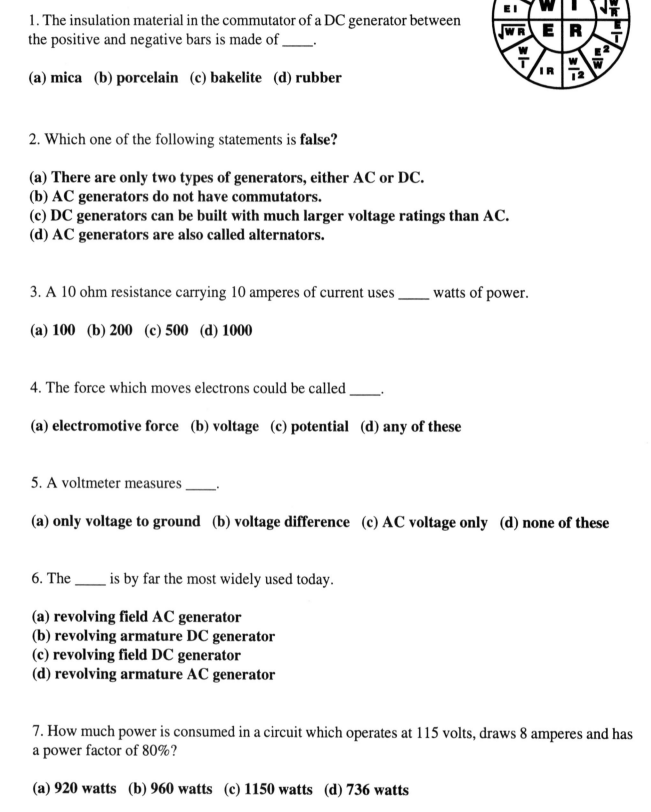

1. The insulation material in the commutator of a DC generator between the positive and negative bars is made of ____.

(a) mica   (b) porcelain   (c) bakelite   (d) rubber

2. Which one of the following statements is **false?**

(a) There are only two types of generators, either AC or DC.
(b) AC generators do not have commutators.
(c) DC generators can be built with much larger voltage ratings than AC.
(d) AC generators are also called alternators.

3. A 10 ohm resistance carrying 10 amperes of current uses ____ watts of power.

(a) 100   (b) 200   (c) 500   (d) 1000

4. The force which moves electrons could be called ____.

(a) electromotive force   (b) voltage   (c) potential   (d) any of these

5. A voltmeter measures ____.

(a) only voltage to ground   (b) voltage difference   (c) AC voltage only   (d) none of these

6. The ____ is by far the most widely used today.

(a) revolving field AC generator
(b) revolving armature DC generator
(c) revolving field DC generator
(d) revolving armature AC generator

7. How much power is consumed in a circuit which operates at 115 volts, draws 8 amperes and has a power factor of 80%?

(a) 920 watts   (b) 960 watts   (c) 1150 watts   (d) 736 watts

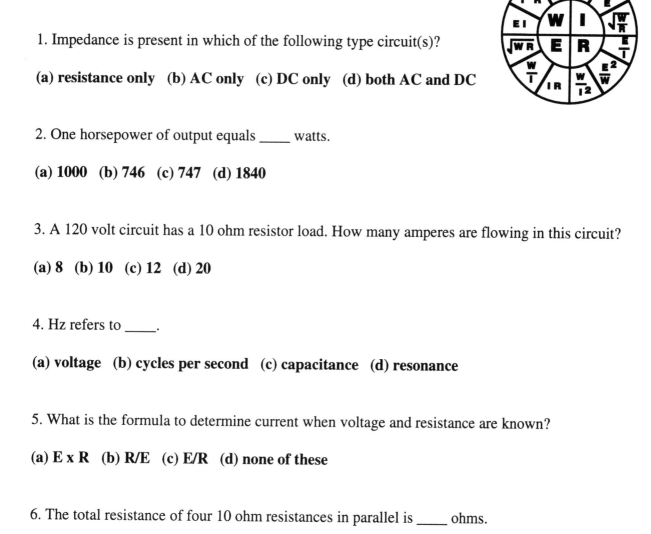

EXAM 8 QUESTIONS

1. Impedance is present in which of the following type circuit(s)?

(a) resistance only   (b) AC only   (c) DC only   (d) both AC and DC

2. One horsepower of output equals ____ watts.

(a) 1000   (b) 746   (c) 747   (d) 1840

3. A 120 volt circuit has a 10 ohm resistor load. How many amperes are flowing in this circuit?

(a) 8   (b) 10   (c) 12   (d) 20

4. Hz refers to ____.

(a) voltage   (b) cycles per second   (c) capacitance   (d) resonance

5. What is the formula to determine current when voltage and resistance are known?

(a) E x R   (b) R/E   (c) E/R   (d) none of these

6. The total resistance of four 10 ohm resistances in parallel is ____ ohms.

(a) 5   (b) 2.5   (c) 6   (d) 40

7. The most heat is created when current flows through which of the following?

(a) a 10 ohm condenser
(b) a 10 ohm inductance coil
(c) a 10 ohm resistor
(d) the heat would be equal

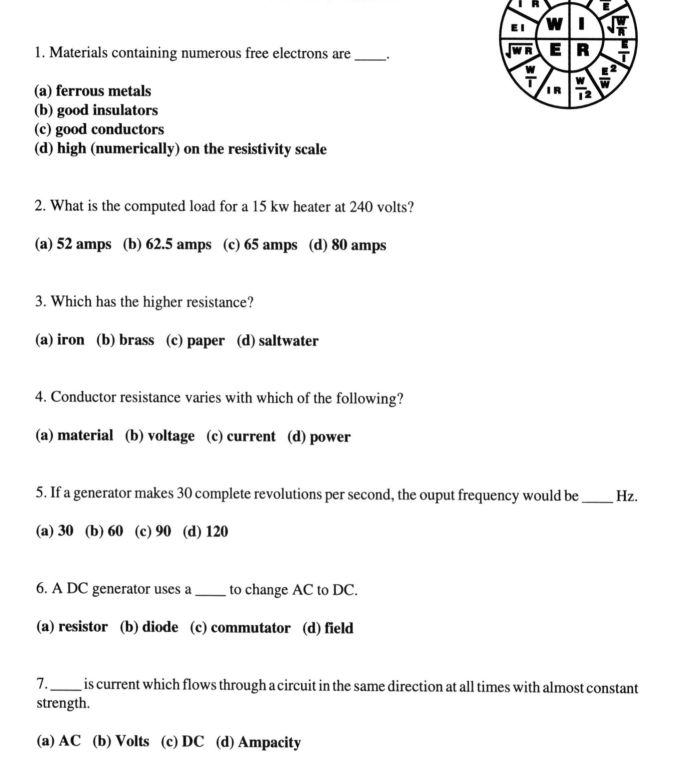

1. Materials containing numerous free electrons are ____.

(a) ferrous metals
(b) good insulators
(c) good conductors
(d) high (numerically) on the resistivity scale

2. What is the computed load for a 15 kw heater at 240 volts?

(a) 52 amps   (b) 62.5 amps   (c) 65 amps   (d) 80 amps

3. Which has the higher resistance?

(a) iron   (b) brass   (c) paper   (d) saltwater

4. Conductor resistance varies with which of the following?

(a) material   (b) voltage   (c) current   (d) power

5. If a generator makes 30 complete revolutions per second, the ouput frequency would be ____ Hz.

(a) 30   (b) 60   (c) 90   (d) 120

6. A DC generator uses a ____ to change AC to DC.

(a) resistor   (b) diode   (c) commutator   (d) field

7. ____ is current which flows through a circuit in the same direction at all times with almost constant strength.

(a) AC   (b) Volts   (c) DC   (d) Ampacity

1. A wattmeter is connected in ____ in the circuit.

(a) series (b) parallel (c) series-parallel (d) none of these

2. When an armature makes one complete _____, it passes through 360 mechanical degrees.

(a) alternation (b) revolution (c) commutation (d) field loop

3. A "mil" measures ____.

(a) .010 (b) .000001 (c) .001 (d) .0100

4. When three equal resistors are connected in parallel the total resistance is ____.

(a) equal to the resistance of each   (b) greater than any one alone
(c) less than any one alone   (d) none of these

5. For voltage and current to be in phase ____.

I. the circuit impedance has only resistance
II. the voltage and current appear at their zero and peak values at the same time

(a) I only (b) II only (c) neither I nor II (d) both I and II

6. If one complete cycle occurs in 1/30 of a second, the frequency is ____ hertz.

(a) 30 (b) 60 (c) 115 (d) 50

7. The revolving armature AC generator is ____ used.

(a) never (b) always (c) usually (d) seldom

EXAM 11 QUESTIONS

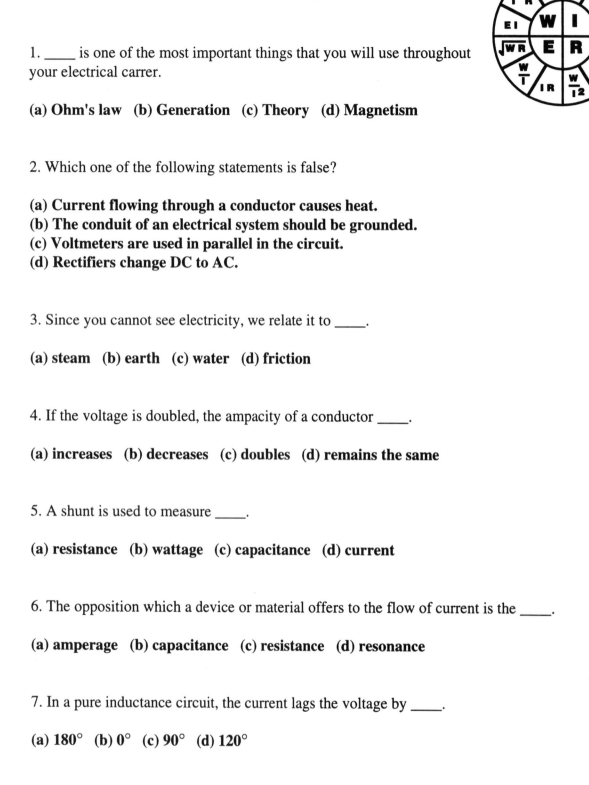

1. ____ is one of the most important things that you will use throughout your electrical carrer.

(a) Ohm's law   (b) Generation   (c) Theory   (d) Magnetism

2. Which one of the following statements is false?

(a) Current flowing through a conductor causes heat.
(b) The conduit of an electrical system should be grounded.
(c) Voltmeters are used in parallel in the circuit.
(d) Rectifiers change DC to AC.

3. Since you cannot see electricity, we relate it to ____.

(a) steam   (b) earth   (c) water   (d) friction

4. If the voltage is doubled, the ampacity of a conductor ____.

(a) increases   (b) decreases   (c) doubles   (d) remains the same

5. A shunt is used to measure ____.

(a) resistance   (b) wattage   (c) capacitance   (d) current

6. The opposition which a device or material offers to the flow of current is the ____.

(a) amperage   (b) capacitance   (c) resistance   (d) resonance

7. In a pure inductance circuit, the current lags the voltage by ____.

(a) 180°   (b) 0°   (c) 90°   (d) 120°

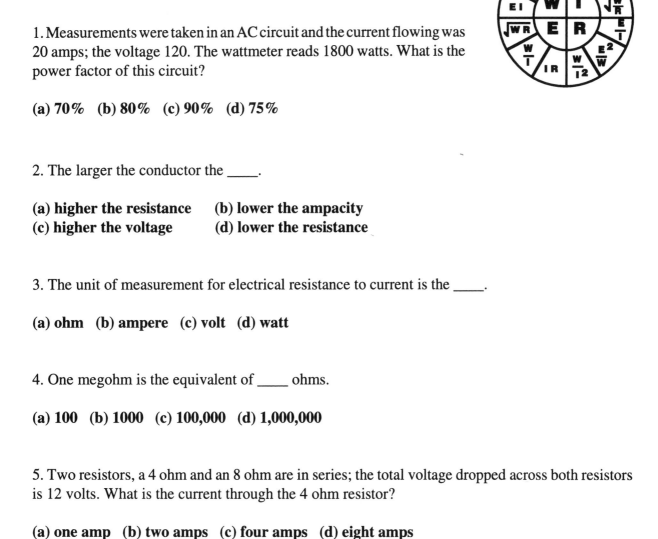

1. Measurements were taken in an AC circuit and the current flowing was 20 amps; the voltage 120. The wattmeter reads 1800 watts. What is the power factor of this circuit?

(a) 70%   (b) 80%   (c) 90%   (d) 75%

2. The larger the conductor the ____.

(a) higher the resistance   (b) lower the ampacity
(c) higher the voltage   (d) lower the resistance

3. The unit of measurement for electrical resistance to current is the ____.

(a) ohm   (b) ampere   (c) volt   (d) watt

4. One megohm is the equivalent of ____ ohms.

(a) 100   (b) 1000   (c) 100,000   (d) 1,000,000

5. Two resistors, a 4 ohm and an 8 ohm are in series; the total voltage dropped across both resistors is 12 volts. What is the current through the 4 ohm resistor?

(a) one amp   (b) two amps   (c) four amps   (d) eight amps

6. Voltage compared to water is like the ____.

(a) pump   (b) pressure   (c) flow   (d) hose

7. When resistors are connected in series, the total resistance is ____.

(a) the sum of the individual resistance values
(b) the equivalent of the smallest resistance value
(c) the equivalent of the largest resistance value
(d) less than the value of the smallest resistance

1. A 1500 watt heater is rated at 230 volts. What would be the wattage if it was connected to a 208 volt source?

(a) 1500 watts   (b) 1350 watts   (c) 1240 watts   (d) 1227 watts

2. Which of the following is a **true** statement?

(a) DC voltage changes are obtained by using series resistors which causes high efficiency
(b) AC armature stator voltages of 750v are common compared to 13,800v for DC generators
(c) The cost of maintenance for DC is considerably less than the costs for AC
(d) DC is used for heavy starting torque and high rate of acceleration loads

3. In a highly inductive AC circuit, what type of device could be put in the circuit to improve the power factor?

(a) resistance   (b) inductance   (c) capacitance   (d) impedance

4. What percentage of the peak voltage is the average voltage?

(a) 70.7%   (b) 71.1%   (c) 63.7%   (d) 62.7%

5. What is the total resistance in this series-parallel circuit?

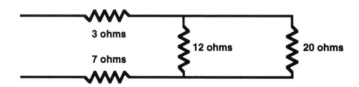

(a) 42 ohms   (b) 4.28 ohms   (c) 17.5 ohms   (d) none of these

6. Doubling the csa of a conductor will _____.

(a) reduce the resistance of the conductor by one-half
(b) double the resistance of the conductor
(c) not change the resistance of the conductor unless the temperature is increased
(d) only effect the resistance in a DC circuit

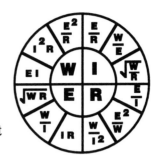

EXAM 14 QUESTIONS

1. The current will lead the voltage when _____.

(a) inductive reactance exceeds the capacitive reactance in the circuit
(b) reactance exceeds the resistance in the circuit
(c) resistance exceeds reactance in the circuit
(d) capacitive reactance exceeds the inductive reactance in the circuit

2. A DC voltmeter may also be used to measure _____

(a) power   (b) frequency   (c) ohms   (d) none of these

3. When converting a percentage to a decimal, move the decimal point two places to the _____ and drop the % sign.

(a) right   (b) left

4. What would happen if the neutral was broken?

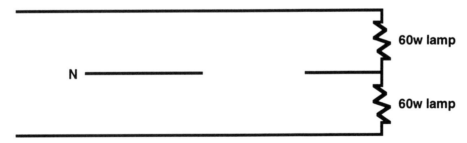

(a) blow a fuse   **(b) burn up lamps**
(c) balanced load, nothing would happen   **(d) voltage difference on each lamp**

5. Horsepower represents the work being done by the _____ of a motor.

(a) input   (b) shaft   (c) drive   (d) output

6. Batteries work under the principle of _____ chemistry.

(a) magnetic   (b) mechanical   (c) electro   (d) photo

1. When three light bulbs are wired in a single fixture, they are connected in ____.

(a) series   (b) series-parallel   (c) parallel   (d) order of wattage

2. Directly proportional means that one factor will be ____ in proportion to an ____ in another factor.

(a) decreased - increase   (b) increased - increase   (c) increased - decrease   (d) none of these

3. Using 1.5 volt dry cells, the voltage between A and B would be ____.

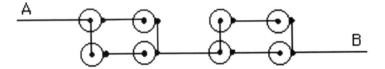

(a) 1.5   (b) 4   (c) 6   (d) 12

4. A generator exciter uses ____ current.

(a) alternating   (b) direct   (c) neither alternating nor direct   (d) either alternating or direct

5. A material is a good conductor if it ____.

(a) has many free electrons   (b) a good insulator   (c) has few free electrons   (d) none of these

6. The square root of 81 is ____.

(a) 40.5   (b) 27   (c) 9   (d) 20.25

7. Electric current will only flow ____.

(a) in an open circuit   (b) in a closed circuit   (c) from positive to negative   (d) in a copper wire

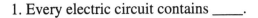

EXAM 16 QUESTIONS

1. Every electric circuit contains _____.

(a) copper wire   (b) high resistance   (c) a power source   (d) a switch

2. When an electric current is forced through a wire that has considerable resistance, the _____.

I. ampacity will decrease   II. voltage will drop   III. wire will heat up

(a) III only   (b) I and II only   (c) II and III only   (d) I and III only

3. Four heaters, each having a resistance of 30 ohms, are connected in series across a 600 volt train circuit. The current is _____ amperes.

(a) 5   (b) 17   (c) 20   (d) 80

4. Which of the following meters is a wattmeter?

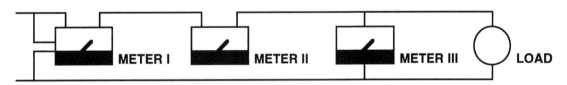

(a) I only   (b) II only   (c) III only   (d) I, II or III

5. A 100 watt light bulb has a resistance of 144Ω, what is the voltage?

(a) 110 volts   (b) 115 volts   (c) 120 volts   (d) 116.4 volts

6. Which of the following statements is **false?**

(a) **Current has only one path to flow in a series circuit**
(b) **In any series circuit the sum of the resistor voltage drops must equal the source voltage**
(c) **In a series circuit the total power is equal to the sum of the wattage dissipated by the individual resistances**
(d) **The total resistance in a series circuit is less than the largest resistor**

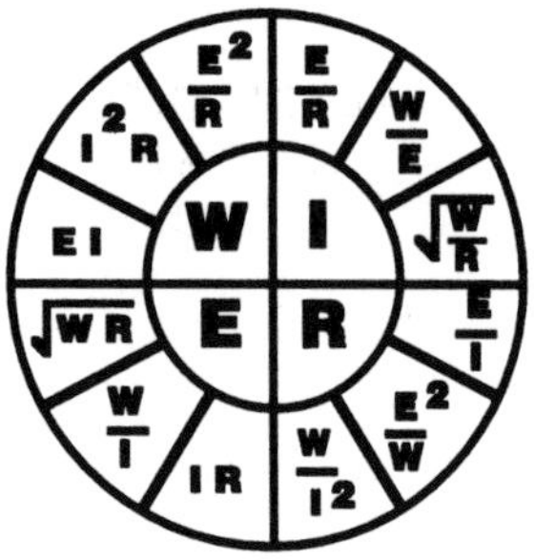

1. The resistance of a circuit may vary due to ____.

(a) a loose connection   (b) a change in voltage
(c) a change in current   (d) induction

2. What is the current in amperes flowing in a circuit that has a 1440 watt load and a resistance of 10Ω?

(a) 8 amps   (b) 10 amps   (c) 12 amps   (d) 20 amps

3. Electrical current is measured in terms of ____.

(a) electron pressure   (b) electrons passing a point per second   (c) watts   (d) resistance

4. The basic unit of electrical work is the ____.

(a) volt-amp   (b) watt   (c) watt hour   (d) kva

5. If the circuit is arranged so that the electrons have only one possible path, the circuit is called a ____ circuit.

(a) shorted   (b) open   (c) parallel   (d) series

6. A 60 cycle current passes through 180 electrical degrees in ____ of a second.

(a) 1/60   (b) 1/90   (c) 1/120   (d) 1/180

7. In a DC circuit, the ratio of watts to voltamperes is always ____.

(a) unity
(b) greater than one
(c) less than one
(d) Cannot tell what it might be

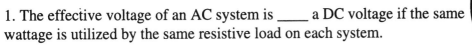

EXAM 18 QUESTIONS

1. The effective voltage of an AC system is _____ a DC voltage if the same wattage is utilized by the same resistive load on each system.

(a) less than   (b) equal to   (c) larger than   (d) a variable compared to

2. A good conductor has _____.

(a) low temperature coefficient   (b) high resistance
(c) low conductance   (d) high conductance

3. In solving series-parallel circuit calculations, you would _____.

(a) work it as a parallel circuit first   (b) treat it as a series circuit
(c) reduce it to its simplest form   (d) assume all loads as equal

4. 450 watts equals how many horsepower?

(a) 1.65   (b) 1/2   (c) .6   (d) 3/4

5. A 15 ohm resistance carrying 20 amperes of current uses _____ watts of power.

(a) 1.3   (b) 300   (c) 4500   (d) 6000

6. Two 500 watt lamps connected in series across a 110 volt line draws 2 amperes. The total power consumed is _____ watts.

(a) 50   (b) 150   (c) 220   (d) 1000

7. What is the total wattage of this circuit?

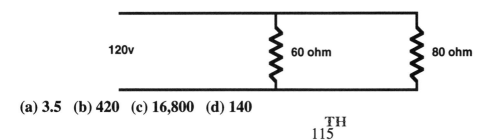

(a) 3.5   (b) 420   (c) 16,800   (d) 140

1. A series circuit will have the same _____ at each load

(a) current   (b) resistance   (c) voltage   (d) wattage

2. A #12 copper wire supplying a 20 amp rated branch circuit may have to carry a maximum of ____ amperes.

(a) 20   (b) 25   (c) 30   (d) several thousand

3. Which one of the following statements is **false?**

(a) A parallel circuit has more than one path for current to flow.
(b) In a parallel circuit the voltage across each load will always be different.
(c) The entire voltage is dropped across each load in a parallel circuit.
(d) In parallel, the current through each resistor will vary depending on the size of each individual resistor.

4. Which one of the following statements is **false?**

(a) In parallel, loads having low resistance will draw more current than loads having a high resistance.
(b) In parallel, loads having high resistance will draw more current than loads having a low resistance.
(c) If parallel loads are connected end-to-end there is more than one path for current to flow.
(d) In parallel, the voltage across each of the resistors will be the same.

5. To solve a problem in a series-parallel circuit it is best to ____.

(a) redraw the circuit and put it in the simplest form
(b) add the sum of the series portion to the sum of the parallel portion
(c) divide the total resistance by 1.732
(d) calculate the current flowing first

6. 60 cycle AC changes direction ____ times per second.

(a) 120   (b) 90   (c) 45   (d) 60

EXAM 20 QUESTIONS

1. If the maximum value of an AC current is 100 amps, the ammeter would read approximately _____ amps.

(a) 100   (b) 80   (c) 70   (d) 50

2. Which one of the following statements is **false?**

(a) **Each load added to a parallel circuit will lower the total resistance.**
(b) **The total current, in parallel, is the sum of each load added collectively.**
(c) **The total resistance, in parallel, is less than any one resistance.**
(d) **Each load added to a series circuit will lower the total resistance.**

3. Unity when referring to power factor is _____.

(a) **.70**   (b) **1.1414**   (c) **.707**   (d) **1.0**

4. Which one of the following statements is **false?**

(a) **There are two types of series loads in a series-parallel circuit.**
(b) **To solve total resistance in a series-parallel circuit always start at the beginning of the sketch.**
(c) **The wattage quadruples when the voltage is doubled.**
(d) **The wattage quadruples when the current is doubled.**

5. When inductance and capacitance are of equal values in a circuit this is called _____.

(a) **reactance**   (b) **resonance**   (c) **impedance**   (d) **resistance**

6. Which one of the following statements is **false?**

(a) **The higher the frequency, the lower the current in a circuit.**
(b) **Pure inductance uses no power.**
(c) **Volt-amps are called wattless power.**
(d) **The symbol letter for impedance is "X".**

1. Computers are considered to be a _____ load.

(a) nonlinear   (b) linear   (c) resistive   (d) capacitive

2. Harmonic simply indicates _____.

(a) an unbalanced circuit
(b) the circuit contains a ballast
(c) the waveform is distorted
(d) lower current flow in the neutral

3. Which one of the following statements is **false?**

(a) Heat is a function of frequency.
(b) AC flows through the csa of the conductor and not on the skin.
(c) Skin effect is an increase in resistance.
(d) Harmonics are additive.

4. The 5th harmonic would be _____ Hz on a 60 Hz AC system.

(a) 60   (b) 90   (c) 180   (d) 300

5. Which one of the following is a **true** statement?

(a) Using a separate neutral for each phase will eliminate the harmonic currents.
(b) A conventional dry-type transformer costs more than a K4 rated transformer.
(c) The neutral conductor supplying discharge lighting can be hotter in temperature than the ungrounded (hot) wire.
(d) K-Factor rated transformers will eliminate harmonic currents.

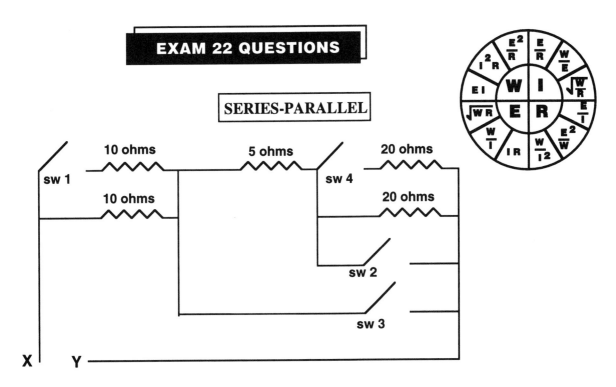

EXAM 22 QUESTIONS

SERIES-PARALLEL

1. With switches 1 and 2 closed, the combined resistance of the circuit is ____ ohms.

(a) 30   (b) 25   (c) 10   (d) 3

2. The switches to be closed in order to obtain a combined resistance of 5 ohms are ____ switches.

(a) 1 and 3   (b) 2 and 3   (c) 1 and 2   (d) 1 and 4

3. If 3 amperes flow through the 5 ohm resistor with all switches open, the voltage between the terminals X and Y is ____ volts.

(a) 15   (b) 60   (c) 90   (d) 105

4. If the line current is 10 amperes with all switches closed, the power consumed in the circuit is ____ watts.

(a) 500   (b) 750   (c) 1000   (d) 2000

5. With only switch 4 closed and a line voltage of 225 volts, the drop across one of the 10 ohm resistors is ____ volts.

(a) 225   (b) 90   (c) 64.3   (d) 56.3

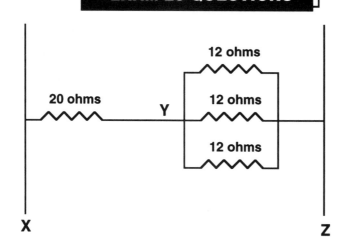

EACH OF THE 12 OHM LOADS IS 2 AMPERES

1. What is the total wattage of the circuit?

(a) 1536w   (b) 864 w   (c) 336w   (d) 192w

2. What is the applied voltage of this circuit?

(a) 144v   (b) 120v   (c) 784v   (d) 336v

3. What is the voltage drop across the 20 ohm series load?

(a) 144v   (b) 24v   (c) 120v   (d) 336v

4. What is the voltage between points **Y** and **Z** ?

(a) 72v   (b) 120v   (c) 24v   (d) 144v

5. What is the wattage of the 20 ohm load?

(a) 120w   (b) 48w   (c) 144w   (d) 720w

6. What is the total wattage of the three 12 ohm loads?

(a) 720w   (b) 768w   (c) 144w   (d) 864w

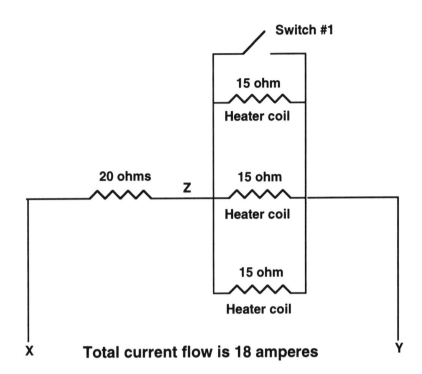

Switch #1

15 ohm

Heater coil

20 ohms   Z   15 ohm

Heater coil

15 ohm

Heater coil

X   **Total current flow is 18 amperes**   Y

1. The equivalent resistance of the three heater coils is _____ ohms.

(a) 5   (b) 10   (c) 15   (d) 45

2. The voltage between point Z and point Y is _____ volts.

(a) 90   (b) 100   (c) 450   (d) 630

3. When switch #1 is closed, the total resistance of the circuit is _____ ohms.

(a) 20   (b) 25   (c) 27.5   (d) 30

4. The total applied voltage is _____ volts.

(a) 90   (b) 100   (c) 450   (d) 630

1. What is the circuit voltage?

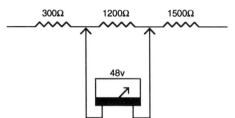

(a) 120 volts   (b) 62.5 volts   (c) 37.5 volts   (d) none of these

2. What is the voltage drop at the 20Ω load?

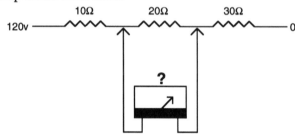

(a) 20 volts   (b) 40 volts   (c) 60 volts   (d) none of these

3. What is the current flowing in the 20Ω load?

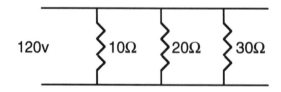

(a) 2 amps   (b) 6 amps   (c) 240 amps   (d) none of these

4. What is the total wattage of the four - 12Ω loads?

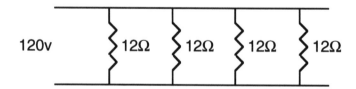

(a) 300 watts   (b) 2400 watts   (c) 4800 watts   (d) none of these

1. What is the power of the four - 12Ω loads?

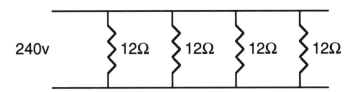

240v   12Ω   12Ω   12Ω   12Ω

(a) 4800 watts   (b) 9600 watts   (c) 19,200 watts   (d) none of these

2. What is the power of the four - 12Ω loads?

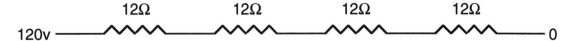

120v   12Ω   12Ω   12Ω   12Ω   0

(a) 300 watts   (b) 25 watts   (c) 4800 watts   (d) none of these

3. The total power given by these four loads would be _____ watts.

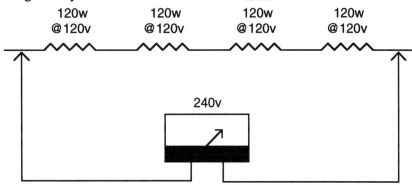

120w
@120v
120w
@120v
120w
@120v
120w
@120v

240v

(a) 240 watts   (b) 480 watts   (c) 120 watts   (d) none of these

4. What is the voltage drop at the 6Ω load?

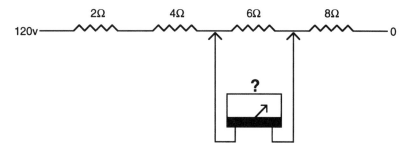

120v   2Ω   4Ω   6Ω   8Ω   0

?

(a) 24 volts   (b) 36 volts   (c) 48 volts   (d) none of these

1. What is the total wattage of the three loads in series?

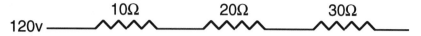

(a) 7200 watts   (b) 240 watts   (c) 960 watts   (d) none of these

2. What is the current flowing in this parallel circuit?

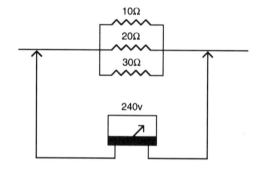

(a) 4 amps   (b) 12 amps   (c) 44 amps   (d) none of these

3. What is the current flowing in this series circuit?

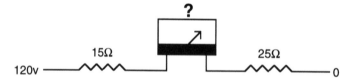

(a) 3 amps   (b) 4.8 amps   (c) 8 amps   (d) none of these

4. The load with the smallest amount of current flowing will be the load of _____ ohms.

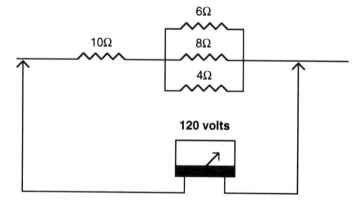

(a) 4   (b) 6   (c) 8   (d) 10

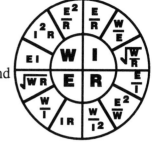

EXAM 28 QUESTIONS

1. Toaster heating elements made of nichrome wire generally have what kind of resistance when compared to copper circuit conductors?

(a) Equal   (b) Lower   (c) Higher   (d) Inversely proportional

2. What is the force that moves electrons from atom to atom through a closed conducting path?

(a) Flux   (b) Resistance   (c) Admittance   (d) EMF

3. A lightning flash is caused by the movement of electrons between the atoms of the atmosphere. The pressure or force that causes those electrons to move is measured in what units?

(a) Magnetic flux   (b) Amperes   (c) Coulombs   (d) Volts

4. A clamp-on ammeter is used, and the reading shown is below half scale. To increase the accuracy, the conductor is looped twice around the jaws. How will this affect the reading?

(a) It will double the previous reading.   (b) It will halve the previous reading.
(c) It will not change the previous reading.   (d) It will give an erroneous reading.

5. The current through the 5Ω resistor is 4 amps, and switches 1, 3, and 4 are closed. What is the voltage across A-B?

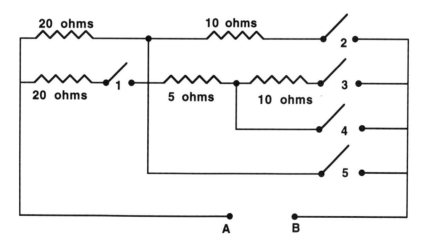

(a) 80 volts   (b) 100 volts   (c) 120 volts   (d) 140 volts

EXAM 29 QUESTIONS

1. Which of the following statements about the purpose or function of an ohmmeter is **TRUE?**

**(a) An ohmmeter uses the power from the system. (b) An ohmmeter requires its own power.
(c) An ohmmeter measures current.   (d) An ohmmeter measures amperage.**

2. A circuit contains two 8-ohm resistors in parallel, and the total current through the circuit is 20 amps. What will be the power utilized by the resistors?

(a) 160 watts   (b) 1,600 watts   (c) 3,200 watts   (d) 6,400 watts

3. An AC circuit produces a constant power with a varying power factor. How will this affect the current?

**(a) It will be lowest at leading power factors.   (b) It will be lowest at lagging power factors.
(c) It will be lowest at unity power factors.   (d) It will be the same at all power factors.**

4. When wattmeter measurements are to be made on high voltage circuits, what must be used?

(a) Multipliers   (b) Instrument transformers   (c) Shunts   (d) Resistors

5. Some materials readily give up electrons and others accept electrons. What is this the basis for?

(a) A magnocouple   (b) A piezometer   (c) A photovoltaic cell   (d) A thermocouple

6. In the sketch shown below the resistance A-B is 20Ω when which switches are open?

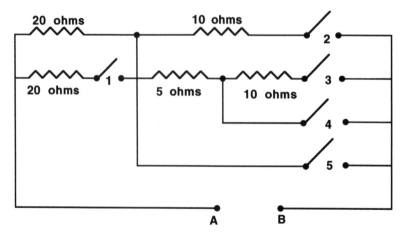

(a) 2 through 5   (b) 1, 2, 4 and 5   (c) 1, 3, 4 and 5   (d) 1, 2, 3 and 4

1. Two lamps are connected in series to a 120-volt source, and each lamp draws 0.62 amps of current. What is the total wattage used in this circuit?

(a) 74.4 watts   (b) 96.8 watts   (c) 120.0 watts   (d) 148.8 watts

2. An appliance is operated on a voltage 10% higher than its nameplate rating. All of the following are results of this **EXCEPT**

(a) shorter appliance life   (b) higher current draw
(c) more power use   (d) significant resistance change

3. In a generator, from a north pole to a south pole and back to a north pole is how many electrical degrees?

(a) 90   (b) 120   (c) 180   (d) 360

4. A constant current of 1 amp being maintained through a resistance by an emf of 1 volt is rated as

(a) 1 coulomb.   (b) 1 foot-pound.   (c) 1 horsepower.   (d) 1 watt.

5. All of the following are resistance heaters **EXCEPT**

(a) an electric blanket.   (b) a toaster.   (c) a hot plate.   (d) a microwave oven.

6. If the resistance is held constant, what happens to the power if the current is doubled?

(a) doubled   (b) halved   (c) multiplied by 4   (d) divided by 4

7. In electrical tests, a megger is calibrated to read ____.

(a) watts   (b) volts   (c) amperes   (d) ohms

8. The property of a circuit or of a material which tends to permit the flow of an electric current is called ____.

(a) inductance   (b) reluctance   (c) conductance   (d) resistance

EXAM 31 QUESTIONS

1. A 5-ampere DC ammeter may be safely used on a 50-ampere circuit provided the ____.

(a) proper size shunt is used   (b) correct size current transformer is used
(c) proper size multiplier is used   (d) proper circuit series resistance is used

2. The difference of electrical potential between two wires of a circuit is its ____.

(a) amperage   (b) voltage   (c) wattage   (d) resistance

3. A coil having 50 turns of #14 wire as compared with a coil of the same diameter but having only 25 turns of #14 wire has ____.

(a) a smaller inductance   (b) a larger inductance
(c) the same inductance   (d) the same impedance

4. Two copper conductors have the same length but the cross-section of one conductor is twice that of the other conductor. If the resistance of the one having a cross-section of twice the other is 10 ohms, the resistance of the other conductor is ____ ohms.

(a) 5   (b) 10   (c) 20   (d) 30

5. A tungsten filament incandescent lamp has its greatest resistance when the lamp is ____.

(a) burning at one-quarter brilliance   (b) burning at half brilliance
(c) burning at full brilliance   (d) cold

6. The difference between a neutral and a grounded circuit conductor is ___.

(a) only a neutral will have equal potential to the ungrounded conductor
(b) only a neutrals outer covering is white or natural gray
(c) only a neutral carries unbalanced current
(d) there is no difference

1. A battery operates on the principle of _____.

(a) photo emission   (b) triboelectric effect   (c) electrochemistry   (d) voltaic conductivity

2. When a switch is closed it has a total resistance of _____.

(a) zero   (b) infinity   (c) unstable   (d) 1500Ω

3. Dielectric is another name for _____.

(a) a conductor   (b) an element   (c) an insulator   (d) a capacitor

4. An open fuse has a resistance of _____.

(a) infinity   (b) zero   (c) approximately 1000Ω   (d) at least 300Ω

5. A wire has a resistance of 5 ohms. What will be the resistance of another wire of the same material three times as long and half the cross sectional area?

(a) 7.5Ω   (b) 15Ω   (c) 30Ω   (d) 50Ω

6. In making a resistance test, remember that the resistance of a short circuit is _____.

(a) approximately zero   (b) midway between high and low
(c) infinite   (d) slightly above the midrange

7. The continuity of a coil of winding may be determined by measuring the resistance of the coil. If the resistance measured is infinite, the coil winding is _____.

(a) partially shorted   (b) totally shorted   (c) open   (d) in good condition

8. The main reason that electrical appliances are connected in parallel rather than series is _____.

(a) appliances connected in series are too noisy
(b) parallel connection is simpler than a series connection
(c) each appliance will draw more current if connected in series
(d) it makes the operation of each appliance independent with each other

1. A circuit with a lagging current means the circuit is _____.

(a) capacitive   (b) reactive   (c) inductive   (d) at resonance

2. A 6 volt lead-acid battery has an internal resistance of 0.01Ω. How much current will flow if the battery has a short circuit?

(a) zero   (b) infinity   (c) 6 amps   (d) 600 amps

3. The wattmeter _____.

(a) has three connections, two of which are used at a time
(b) can measure DC power but not 60 Hz AC power
(c) has voltage and current coils to measure real power
(d) measures apparent reactive power and resistance

4. A 25 watt incandescent bulb rated @120v and operated on a 120v line has burnt out and has to be replaced as soon as possible. There are several lamps available but not of the same rating. Which of the bulbs below should be used to approximate the power consumtion of the burnt out bulb?

(a) 20 watts @110v   (b) 100 watts @240v   (c) 50 watts @240v   (d) 75 watts @220v

5. A single-phase motor is taking 20 amperes from a 400 volt supply at 0.75 lagging power factor. The power taken is _____ watts.

(a) 2,000   (b) 4,000   (c) 6,000   (d) 8,000

6. Three parallel branches of 10, 20 and 30 ohms respectively are connected across a 60 volt DC supply. The total power consumed by these resistors is _____ watts.

(a) 560   (b) 600   (c) 606   (d) 660

EXAM 34 QUESTIONS

1. The hot resistance of an incandescent lamp is 10 ohms and the rated voltage is 50 volts. Find the series resistance required to operate the lamp from an 80 volt supply.

(a) 4Ω (b) 6Ω (c) 8Ω (d) 10Ω

2. A relay has a resistance of 30 ohms and an operating current of 0.8 amps. The power to operate the relay is _____ watts.

(a) 19.2 (b) 24 (c) 37.5 (d) none of these

3. A parallel circuit has three branches of 12, 4 and 16 ohms respectively. If a 4 amp current flows in the 12 ohm branch, the total current supplied to the three branches would be _____ amps.

(a) 16 (b) 20 (c) 24 (d) none of these

4. A circuit that has infinite resistance is called a/an _____ circuit.

(a) short (b) ground (c) open (d) all of these

5. A component having no continuity would have _____ resistance.

(a) zero (b) small (c) infinite (d) all of these

6. A good fuse will have _____ resistance.

(a) zero (b) small (c) infinite (d) all of these

7. The physical size of a resistor that determines the ability of the resistor to absorb heat is rated in _____.

(a) ohms (b) watts (c) farads (d) volts

8. Capacitors can be tested by _____.

(a) bridging (b) a spark test (c) an ohmmeter (d) all of these

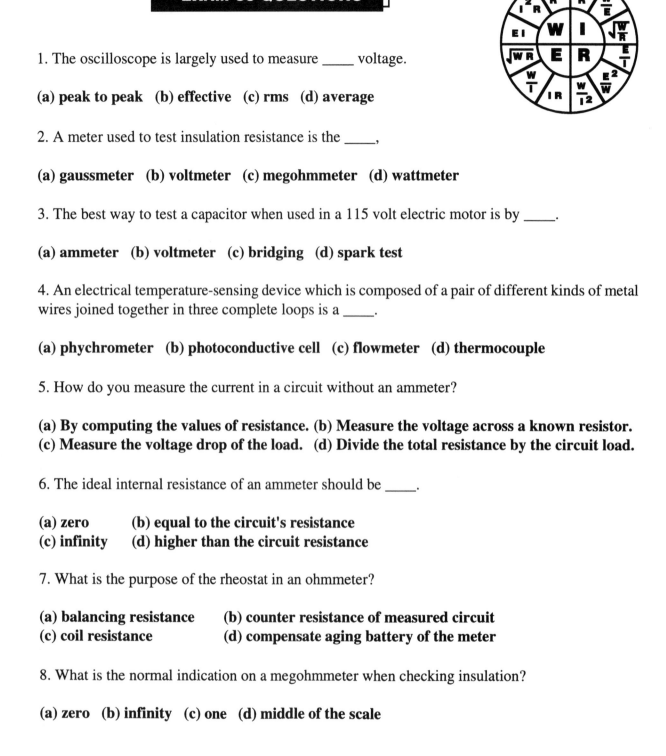

EXAM 35 QUESTIONS

1. The oscilloscope is largely used to measure _____ voltage.

(a) peak to peak   (b) effective   (c) rms   (d) average

2. A meter used to test insulation resistance is the _____,

(a) gaussmeter   (b) voltmeter   (c) megohmmeter   (d) wattmeter

3. The best way to test a capacitor when used in a 115 volt electric motor is by _____.

(a) ammeter   (b) voltmeter   (c) bridging   (d) spark test

4. An electrical temperature-sensing device which is composed of a pair of different kinds of metal wires joined together in three complete loops is a _____.

(a) phychrometer   (b) photoconductive cell   (c) flowmeter   (d) thermocouple

5. How do you measure the current in a circuit without an ammeter?

**(a) By computing the values of resistance. (b) Measure the voltage across a known resistor.
(c) Measure the voltage drop of the load.   (d) Divide the total resistance by the circuit load.**

6. The ideal internal resistance of an ammeter should be _____.

**(a) zero   (b) equal to the circuit's resistance
(c) infinity   (d) higher than the circuit resistance**

7. What is the purpose of the rheostat in an ohmmeter?

**(a) balancing resistance   (b) counter resistance of measured circuit
(c) coil resistance   (d) compensate aging battery of the meter**

8. What is the normal indication on a megohmmeter when checking insulation?

(a) zero   (b) infinity   (c) one   (d) middle of the scale

VOLTAGE DROP

CALCULATIONS

VOLTAGE DROP

To successfully calculate voltage drop you must first understand Ohm's Law and the equations.

At the beginning, every electron has been given energy by the source (generator). As the electron moves through the circuit it uses up this energy (usually in a form of heat). When it arrives back at the source it has used up all of its energy and more electrons must be supplied by the source. Thus, keeping the voltage constant as the energy is being used up.

Kirchhoff's Voltage Law applied to a simple series circuit states: "The sum of the voltage drop is equal to the source voltage".

In a series circuit a **portion** of the source voltage is dropped across each series load. The sum of these voltage drops would equal the source voltage.

When loads are connected in parallel, voltage is also dropped across each load. Instead of a part of the source voltage being dropped across each load, as with the series circuit, in a parallel circuit **all** of the source voltage is dropped across **each load**. The reason is that loads connected in parallel are connected directly across the source voltage.

Example:

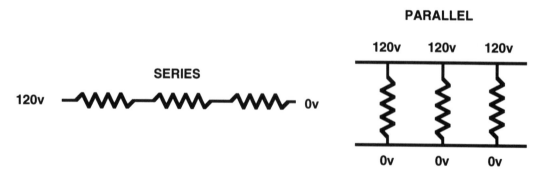

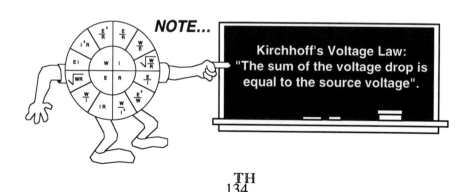

Remember, voltage is a difference of potential between **two points**.

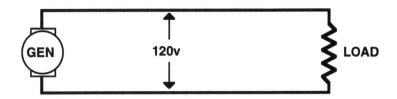

This voltage is constantly being supplied by the generator to maintain a constant source voltage.

The basic elements of the electric circuit are the source, the conductors, and the load.

Power (watts) is the rate at which work is being done. There are two types of work:

1. **USEFUL WORK**
2. **WASTED WORK** (dissipated)

Watts = I^2R Watts = Heat

This I^2R heating takes place in the conductors as in the load.

Useful work would be an appliance such as an electric range, the I^2R heating is needed and is not considered wasted power. Another example of useful work is the light bulb. The wattage or power is a measure of the I^2R heating of the filament of the bulb which depends on the fixed resistance of the filament.

With the load little, can be done about the I^2R heating, as the load current and resistance value cannot usually be changed without affecting the operation. The **load is useful work**.

Wasted work is the heating of the **conductors** supplying the energy to the load. The conductors have a resistance to the flow of current.

The voltage at the **load** can never be the same as the **source** voltage due to the **resistance of the conductors**.

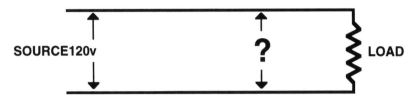

The resistance of the circuit conductors causes a **voltage drop** to the source voltage. How much the source voltage will drop depends on the load and the resistance in the circuit.

Voltage drop = I x R

The voltage drop in a conductor is a **percentage** of the source voltage. If conductors had **zero resistance**, there would be no voltage drop between the load and the source. This is not possible as all matter has resistance.

Voltage drop can be defined as **wasted work in heating the conductors**. The generation of electrical energy costs money, therefore it is important to keep wasted work at a minimum.

A larger size conductor in circular-mil area will have a lower resistance and less voltage drop. As a contractor, using the largest possible conductor size is neither practical nor economical, as an increase in one or two conductor sizes can raise the overall cost of a job to where it is no longer competitive.

Voltage drop in a circuit can be designed from a practical wiring standpoint not to exceed a certain **percentage** of the applied source voltage.

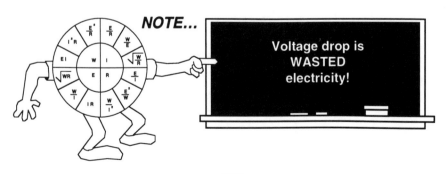

The Code recommends a branch-circuit voltage drop of not more than 3% of the source voltage and a total voltage drop not to exceed 5%.

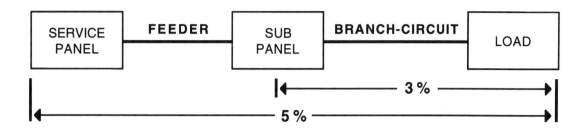

Maximum of 3% voltage drop on the branch circuit.

Example: If the feeder has an actual voltage drop of 1%, the branch circuit is still limited to 3% voltage drop. On a branch circuit, the Code recommends a voltage drop not to exceed 3% of the source voltage. The **voltage drop permitted** on a branch circuit changes with the source voltage.

Example:

SOURCE VOLTAGE	3% PERMITTED VOLTAGE DROP
115 volts	3.45 volts
120 volts	3.6 volts
208 volts	6.24 volts
230 volts	6.9 volts
240 volts	7.2 volts
480 volts	14.4 volts

To find the voltage drop of a circuit use the formula VD = I x R.

I = The load current flowing in the conductor in amps.

R = The resistance in ohms of the conductor. The resistance values of conductors are found in Chapter 9, Table 8 of the Code. Table 8 indicates the resistance of a conductor in ohms per 1000 feet.

Table 8. Conductor Properties

Size AWG / kcmil	Area Circ. Mils	Stranding Quan-tity	Stranding Diam. In.	Overall Diam. In.	Overall Area In.²	Copper Uncoated ohm / kFT	Copper Coated ohm / kFT	Aluminum ohm / kFT
18	1620	1	—	0.040	0.001	7.77	8.08	12.8
18	1620	7	0.015	0.046	0.002	7.95	8.45	13.1
16	2580	1	—	0.051	0.002	4.89	5.08	8.05
16	2580	7	0.019	0.058	0.003	4.99	5.29	8.21
14	4110	1	—	0.064	0.003	3.07	3.19	5.06
14	4110	7	0.024	0.073	0.004	3.14	3.26	5.17
12	6530	1	—	0.081	0.005	1.93	2.01	3.18
12	6530	7	0.030	0.092	0.006	1.98	2.05	3.25
10	10380	1	—	0.102	0.008	1.21	1.26	2.00
10	10380	7	0.038	0.116	0.011	1.24	1.29	2.04
8	16510	1	—	0.128	0.013	0.764	0.786	1.26
8	16510	7	0.049	0.146	0.017	0.778	0.809	1.28
6	26240	7	0.061	0.184	0.027	0.491	0.510	0.808
4	41740	7	0.077	0.232	0.042	0.308	0.321	0.508
3	52620	7	0.087	0.260	0.053	0.245	0.254	0.403
2	66360	7	0.097	0.292	0.067	0.194	0.201	0.319
1	83690	19	0.066	0.332	0.087	0.154	0.160	0.253
1/0	105600	19	0.074	0.373	0.109	0.122	0.127	0.201
2/0	133100	19	0.084	0.419	0.138	0.0967	0.101	0.159
3/0	167800	19	0.094	0.470	0.173	0.0766	0.0797	0.126
4/0	211600	19	0.106	0.528	0.219	0.0608	0.0626	0.100
250	—	37	0.082	0.575	0.260	0.0515	0.0535	0.0847
300	—	37	0.090	0.630	0.312	0.0429	0.0446	0.0707
350	—	37	0.097	0.681	0.364	0.0367	0.0382	0.0605
400	—	37	0.104	0.728	0.416	0.0321	0.0331	0.0529
500	—	37	0.116	0.813	0.519	0.0258	0.0265	0.0424
600	—	61	0.992	0.893	0.626	0.0214	0.0223	0.0353
700	—	61	0.107	0.964	0.730	0.0184	0.0189	0.0303
750	—	61	0.111	0.998	0.782	0.0171	0.0176	0.0282
800	—	61	0.114	1.03	0.834	0.0161	0.0166	0.0265
900	—	61	0.122	1.09	0.940	0.0143	0.0147	0.0235
1000	—	61	0.128	1.15	1.04	0.0129	0.0132	0.0212
1250	—	91	0.117	1.29	1.30	0.0103	0.0106	0.0169
1500	—	91	0.128	1.41	1.57	0.00858	0.00883	0.0141
1750	—	127	0.117	1.52	1.83	0.00735	0.00735	0.0121
2000	—	127	0.126	1.63	2.09	0.00643	0.00662	0.0106

The resistances shown are based on 75°C or 167°F.

The first column shows the AWG (American Wire Gauge) size.

The second column shows the area of circular mils (cma). A circular mil is 0.001 inch.

The third column shows the quantity of stranding, 1 strand is a solid wire, whereas 7 strands means stranded wire.

The last three columns show the resistance for 1000 feet of wire. Uncoated copper, coated copper (tinned), and aluminum.

Using Table 8 you will find a #12 **solid uncoated** copper conductor has a resistance of 1.93 ohms per 1000 feet. A #12 **stranded uncoated** copper conductor has a resistance of 1.98 ohms per 1000 feet. A #12 solid **aluminum** has a resistance of 3.18 ohms per 1000 feet. A copper conductor has less resistance than an aluminum conductor.

As you work voltage drop calculations it is very important to make sure the conductor is either solid or stranded, coated or uncoated, or aluminum. The resistance is different for each as indicated in Table 8.

Table 8 shows that a conductor larger in size (AWG) has less resistance.

Example: A #6 uncoated copper has a resistance of 0.491 ohms per k/ft which is less resistance than 1.98 ohms for a #12 stranded uncoated copper.

Doubling the circular mil area of a conductor actually reduces the resistance one-half.

Example: A #500 kcmil uncoated copper has a resistance of 0.0258 ohms per k/ft. If you double the cma to #1000 kcmil the resistance for uncoated copper is 0.0129 ohms per k/ft or divide 0.0258Ω by two: .0258/2 = 0.0129Ω (one-half the resistance of a #500 kcmil)

To find the resistance of the wire in a branch circuit, first find the resistance per 1000 feet from Table 8 for the size and type of wire. Then multiply the resistance per k/ft by the total length of wire. Place a decimal point **3 places** to the left of the total length of wire for thousandths.

Example: Find the resistance for 150 feet of #12 solid uncoated copper wire.

Solution: First step is turn to Table 8 and find the resistance for 1000 feet = 1.93 ohms. Now multiply 1.93 ohms by .150 feet = **.2895 ohms** resistance for 150 feet.

Example: Find the resistance for 98 feet of #2/0 aluminum wire.

Solution: First step is turn to Table 8 and find the resistance for 1000 feet = 0.159 ohms. Now multiply 0.159 ohms by .098 feet = **0.015582 ohms**.

Calculate the voltage drop in the following circuit using the formula VD = I x R:

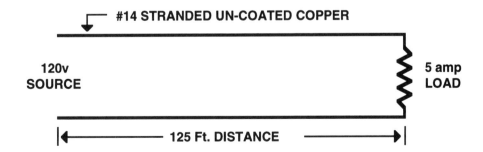

Solution: Using the formula VD = I x R, I is given as 5 amps, all that is left to find is R. Turn to Table 8 and it shows a #14 stranded uncoated copper conductor at 3.14 ohms per k/ft; multiply 3.14 ohms by .250 feet of wire = **.785 ohms**. Remember the sketch shows 125 feet **distance one-way**. The length of the wire for this circuit would require **250 feet**.

I = 5 amps   R = .785 ohms   VD = 5 amps x .785 ohms = **3.925 volts dropped**

The voltage **at the load** would be the source voltage of 120 minus 3.925v = 116.075v at the load.

This branch circuit **violates** the Code recommendation of 3% maximum, 120v x 3% = 3.6 maximum voltage drop permitted.

There are ways to lower voltage drop:
Increase the conductor size, shorten the distance, lower the current in the load, increase the voltage.

Most often increasing the conductor size is the **only** choice you have, as your customer has already determined the distance and the load.

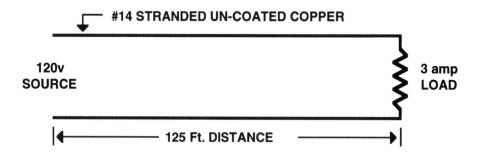

#14 STRANDED UN-COATED COPPER

120v
SOURCE

3 amp
LOAD

125 Ft. DISTANCE

If, the load could be **reduced** to 3 amps, VD = I x R = 3 amps x .785 ohms = 2.355 volts dropped. Now the branch circuit is within the maximum 3% or 3.6 volts dropped permitted.

But often a load **can't** be reduced. **If,** the distance was less, 100 feet instead of 125 feet, at 100 feet in distance, the branch circuit would have a total length of wire of 200 feet.

3.14 ohms x .200 feet = .628 ohms. VD = 5 amp x .628 ohm = 3.14 volts dropped. Now the branch circuit is within the 3% or 3.6 VD permitted by the Code, **but** often a distance **can't** be less.

If, a larger wire was used, a #12 instead of a #14; Table 8 shows a #12 stranded uncoated copper at 1.98 ohms per k/ft x .250 feet = .495 ohms resistance. VD = 5 amp x .495 ohms = 2.475 volts dropped. Now the branch circuit is within the 3% or 3.6 VD permitted.

Reducing voltage drop in a branch circuit by using a larger conductor is usually the choice made and usually the **only** choice you have.

Some branch circuit loads are dual voltage rated. You have a choice, you can connect the load to 120 volts **or** 240 volts.

By connecting to 240 volts, the load would be reduced one-half from 5 amps to 2.5 amps. The voltage drop permitted would increase from the 3% of 120 = 3.6v to 3% of 240v = 7.2 VD permitted.

VD = 2.5 amps x .785 ohms resistance = 1.9625 volts dropped, well within the permitted 7.2 volts.

Summary: The branch circuit at 120 volt source had a current of 5 amps and a voltage drop of 3.925 volts which is 3.925v/120v = 3.27% which exceeds the Code recommendation of 3%.

By **doubling** the voltage from 120v to 240v the current is half and the voltage drop is 1.9625v/240v = .81% (not even 1%).

To give you an idea of how a higher voltage can improve the voltage drop and how much farther in distance you can install this same branch circuit, the distance could be increased to 500 feet instead of 125 feet. Now the branch circuit has 1000 feet (2 x 500') of #14 stranded uncoated copper. Table 8 shows a resistance of 3.14 ohms for 1000 feet. VD = I x R; 2.5 amps x 3.14 ohms = 7.85 volts dropped. Just **over** the Code recommendation of 240v x 3% = 7.2 volts - but look at the distance!!

On the following page I've included all of the voltage drop formulas.

The Code suggests in sections 210.19(A) FPN, and 215.2(B) FPN keeping voltage drop at **3% for branch circuits** and **5% total** will provide reasonable efficiency of operation.

Voltage drop is **wasted electricity** due to heating the conductors. $\boxed{\text{Power Loss} = \text{VD} \times \text{I}}$

To find:

VOLTAGE DROP ...... $VD = \dfrac{2 \times K \times D \times I}{CM}$ (or) $VD = I \times R$

WIRE SIZE .... $CM = \dfrac{2 \times \textcircled{K} \times D \times I}{VD \text{ permitted}}$

DISTANCE .... $D = \dfrac{CM \times VD \text{ permitted}}{2 \times K \times I}$

LOAD .... $I = \dfrac{CM \times VD \text{ permitted}}{2 \times K \times D}$

* The "2" in the formulas is for single-phase circuits, this is the conductor to and from the load

* For 3 phase voltage drop calculations, change the "2" in the formula to **1.732**

* "K" is the resistance of a circular mil-foot. Exact $K = \dfrac{R \times CM}{1000'}$

* When using the formula to find "WIRE SIZE" use the **approximate $\textcircled{K}$ factor** of 12.9 for copper and 21.2 for aluminum

* "D" is the distance **one way** in a circuit

* "I" is the load in amperes. For motors use the Full Load Current from the motor tables

* "CM" is the size of conductor in circular mils, found only in Table 8

* "VD permitted" is the **percentage of the applied source voltage,** 3% of the source for a branch circuit and 5% of the total applied to the system. Example: On a branch circuit that has a source voltage of 120 the voltage drop permitted would be 120v x 3% = 3.6 volts. Example: On a branch circuit that has a source voltage of 208 the voltage drop permitted would be 208v x 3% = 6.24v. Example: A system with an applied voltage of 240 the **total** voltage drop permitted on the entire service would be 240v x 5% = 12 volts.

I teach in my Code classes to calculate the exact K. It takes only a few seconds with a calculator and using Table 8, and it could be the difference of choosing the right answer on the exam.

Sometimes an **approximate K** factor is used, but only when determining the conductor **size**.

K represents the resistance of a circular mil foot of conductor. Referred to as the resistivity factor of conductor metal. A circular mil foot is .001", 12 inches in length.

We know for a fact that resistance changes with the **size** of the conductor, so "K" will also be a **different** resistance value for **each** conductor size.

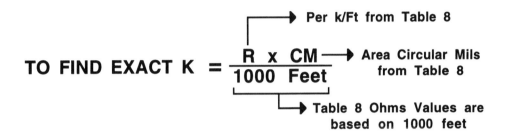

$$\text{TO FIND EXACT K} = \frac{\text{R} \times \text{CM}}{1000 \text{ Feet}}$$

Per k/Ft from Table 8

Area Circular Mils from Table 8

Table 8 Ohms Values are based on 1000 feet

Using the formula above we can find the exact K factor for a #12 solid uncoated copper conductor:

$$\frac{1.93 \text{ ohms} \times 6530 \text{ cm}}{1000 \text{ feet}} = \mathbf{12.6029}$$

The exact K factor for a #12 solid aluminum conductor would be:

$$\frac{3.18 \text{ ohms} \times 6530 \text{ cm}}{1000 \text{ feet}} = \mathbf{20.7654}$$

Example: What is the voltage drop in the following branch circuit? Use **both** formulas for voltage drop and compare for **exact** same answer.

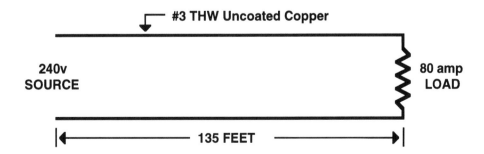

#3 THW Uncoated Copper

240v
SOURCE

80 amp
LOAD

|◄─────── 135 FEET ───────►|

Let's start by using the formula VD = I x R.

I = 80 amps
R = (Table 8) 0.245 ohms per k/ft x .270 feet (2 x 135') = 0.06615 ohm
VD = I x R   80 amps x 0.06615 ohm = **5.292 volts dropped**.

Now use the formula $VD = \dfrac{2 \times K \times D \times I}{CM}$

The first step is to find the exact K factor:

$\dfrac{.245 \text{ ohm} \times 52,620 \text{ cm}}{1000 \text{ feet}} = 12.8919$

$VD = \dfrac{2 \times 12.8919 \times 135' \times 80 \text{ amps}}{52,620 \text{ cm}}$ = **5.292 volts dropped**.

By using the **exact K** factor you have the **exact** same answer of 5.292 volts dropped by using either formula.

•Note: When using the VD = I x R formula remember you are using the **total length of the conductor** in the branch circuit which is the distance of 135 feet times 2 = 270 feet of conductor. Formula VD $= \dfrac{2 \times K \times D \times I}{CM}$ the"2" in this formula takes care of the total length of conductor as it is multiplied by the "D" in this formula. "D" is the distance one way. In this branch circuit the "D" is 135 feet and by using "2" in the formula = 270 feet.

So far we have been calculating voltage drop in a single-phase branch circuit. Now let's switch to a **three-phase branch circuit**. In the formulas change the "2" to **1.732** for three-phase calculations. The advantage is the 1.732 which is the square root of 3. We don't have to calculate the total resistance of three conductors. We are calculating the length of **one conductor** times 1.732.

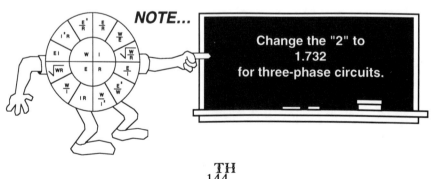

NOTE...

Change the "2" to
1.732
for three-phase circuits.

3 ø VOLTAGE DROP FORMULAS

$$VD = I \times R \times 1.732$$

Length of
one conductor

$$VD = \frac{1.732 \times K \times D \times I}{CM}$$

Let's calculate the voltage drop in the following **three-phase** branch circuit supplying a 20 amp load.

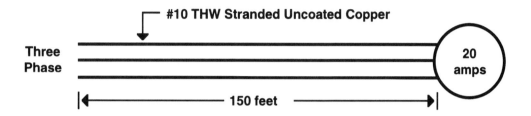

#10 THW Stranded Uncoated Copper

Three
Phase

20
amps

|← ——————— 150 feet ——————— →|

Using the formula $VD = I \times R \times 1.732$; I = 20 amps; R = Table 8 shows a resistance of 1.24 ohms per 1000 feet for a #10 stranded uncoated copper conductor. Next step is to find the resistance of **one** conductor, 150 feet in length. 1.24 ohms x .150 feet = .186 ohms.

$VD = I \times R \times 1.732$ 20 amps x .186 ohms x 1.732 = **6.44 volts dropped**.

Now let's use the formula $VD = \dfrac{1.732 \times K \times D \times I}{CM}$

First step is to find exact K:

Exact $K = \dfrac{R \times CM}{1000'} = \dfrac{1.24\Omega \times 10380 \text{ cm}}{1000'} = 12.8712$

$VD = \dfrac{1.732 \times 12.8712 \times 150' \times 20 \text{ amps}}{10380 \text{ cm}} = $ **6.44 volts dropped**.

•Note: We have been calculating the voltage drop in single-phase and three-phase branch circuits using the formulas for VD. On the following pages we will use formulas to find WIRE SIZE, DISTANCE, and MAXIMUM LOAD.

$$\text{USE APPROXIMATE}$$

WIRE SIZE – – – – – – $CM = \dfrac{2 \times K \times D \times I}{VD \text{ permitted}}$

DISTANCE – – – – – – – $D = \dfrac{CM \times VD \text{ permitted}}{2 \times K \times I}$

LOAD – – – – – – – – – – $I = \dfrac{CM \times VD \text{ permitted}}{2 \times K \times D}$

* For the Three-Phase:
change the "2" in the
formulas to 1.732

** For the CM Formula:
use an approximate K factor of
12.9 for Copper and
21.2 for Aluminum

The key to solving exam questions is to recognize the **key** word in the question. The key word will tell you which formula to use.

Example: What size THW conductor is required for a 208 volt single-phase branch circuit that has a 20 amp load, located 175 feet from the source? The **key** word is **size**. Use the formula to find wire **SIZE** ...cm.

The question did not mention copper or aluminum conductors, NEC Article 110.5 states you shall use **copper** unless aluminum is specified.

NOTE...

Look for the KEY WORD in the question to select the formula!

Use the formula CM = $\frac{2 \times K \times D \times I}{VD\ permitted}$

CM = $\frac{2 \times \textbf{12.9} \times 175' \times 20\ amp}{6.24\ VD\ per\ (3\%\ of\ 208v)}$ = 14, 471 cm required

Turn to Table 8 and select a conductor that has **at least** 14,471 cm. The answer is a **#8** conductor which has 16,510 cm. When selecting the conductor size from Table 8 circular mil area, also remember the conductor size selected for voltage drop must also be capable of carrying the maximum current required. NEC Table 310.16 shows a #8 THW copper conductor with a normal ampacity of 50, so the answer #8 THW is correct.

Example: How far from a single-phase 240 volt source can you install a #10 solid aluminum conductor to a branch circuit with a 15 amp load?

Solution: The key word is "far"; use the formula to find D. First step is to find the exact K for a #10 solid aluminum.

Exact K = $\frac{2.0 \times 10380\ cm}{1000'}$ = 20.76

Use formula: D = $\frac{10380\ cm \times 7.2\ VD\ per}{2 \times 20.76 \times 15\ amps}$ = **120 feet**.

Example: What is the maximum load permitted on a 120 volt single-phase branch circuit using #12 stranded uncoated copper conductors, 125 feet from the source?

Solution: The key word is "load"; use the formula to find I. First step is to find the exact K for a #12 stranded uncoated copper conductor.

Exact K = $\frac{1.98\Omega \times 6530\ cm}{1000'}$ = 12.9294

Use formula: I = $\frac{6530\ cm \times 3.6\ VD\ per}{2 \times 12.9294 \times 125'}$ = **7.27 amps**

NOTE... When calculating the SIZE of a conductor for CM, remember to check for AMPACITY also!

So far we have been using Table 8 at the resistance values given @ 75°C. Both Table 8 and Table 9 are based on values at 75°C. A THW or RHW conductor are 75°C conductors per Table 310.13 or Table 310.16 listings. When using Table 8 or 9 for conductors with a higher insulation rating than 75°C, the resistance must be **increased**. For conductors with a rating **less** than the Table value of 75°C, the resistance can be **reduced**.

Table 310.16. Allowable Ampacities of Insulated Conductors
Rated 0-2000 Volts, 60°to 90°C (140°to 194°F)
Not More Than THree Conductors in Raceway or Cable or Earth
(Directly Buried), Based on Ambient Temperature of 30°C (86°F).

Size	Temperature Rating of Conductor. See Table 310.13.						Size
	60°C (140°F)	75°C (167°F)	90°C (194°F)	60°C (140°F)	75°C (167°F)	90°C (194°F)	
AWG kcmil	TYPES TW, UF	TYPES FEPW, RHW, THHW, THW, THWN, XHHW, USE, ZW	TYPES TA, TBS,SA, SIS, FEP, FEPB, MI RHH, RHW-2, THHN, THHW, THW-2, THWN-2 XHHW, USE-2	TYPES TW, UF	TYPES RHW, THHW, THW, THWN, XHHW, USE	TYPES TA, TBS, SA, SIS, THHN, THHW, THW-2, THWN-2, RHH, RHW-2, USE-2, XHH, XHHW, XHHW-2, ZW-2	AWG kcmil
	COPPER			ALUMINUM OR COPPER-CLAD ALUMINUM			
18	....	....	14	....	....	....	....
16	....	....	18	....	....	....	....
14*	20	20	25	....	....	....	....
12*	25	25	30	20	20	25	12*
10*	30	35	40	25	30	35	10*
8	40	50	55	30	40	45	8

Types TW and UF are 60°C rated conductors; RHW, THW and RH are 75°C rated conductors; whereas THHN and RHH are 90°C rated.

So the difference in temperature from 60°C to 75°C is **15°** and from 75°C to 90°C is also a **15°** change in temperature.

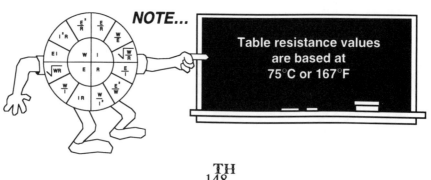

NOTE...

Table resistance values
are based at
75°C or 167°F

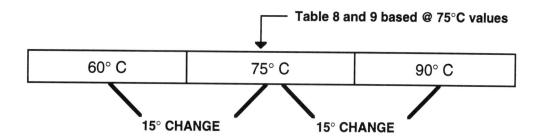

Table 8 and 9 based @ 75°C values

| 60° C | 75° C | 90° C |

15° CHANGE   15° CHANGE

Table 8. Conductor Properties

| Size AWG / kcmil | Area Circ. Mils | Conductors | | | | DC Resistance at 75°C (167°F) | | |
| | | Stranding | | Overall | | Copper | | Alumi-num |
		Quan-tity	Diam. In.	Diam. In.	Area In.²	Uncoated ohm / kFT	Coated ohm / kFT	ohm / kFT
18	1620	1	—	0.040	0.001	7.77	8.08	12.8
18	1620	7	0.015	0.046	0.002	7.95	8.45	13.1
16	2580	1	—	0.051	0.002	4.89	5.08	8.05
16	2580	7	0.019	0.058	0.003	4.99	5.29	8.21
14	4110	1	—	0.064	0.003	3.07	3.19	5.06
14	4110	7	0.024	0.073	0.004	3.14	3.26	5.17
12	6530	1	—	0.081	0.005	1.93	2.01	3.18
12	6530	7	0.030	0.092	0.006	1.98	2.05	3.25
10	10380	1	—	0.102	0.008	1.21	1.26	2.00
10	10380	7	0.038	0.116	0.011	1.24	1.29	2.04
8	16510	1	—	0.128	0.013	0.764	0.786	1.26
8	16510	7	0.049	0.146	0.017	0.778	0.809	1.28
6	26240	7	0.061	0.184	0.027	0.491	0.510	0.808
4	41740	7	0.077	0.232	0.042	0.308	0.321	0.508
3	52620	7	0.087	0.260	0.053	0.245	0.254	0.403
2	66360	7	0.097	0.292	0.067	0.194	0.201	0.319
1	83690	19	0.066	0.332	0.087	0.154	0.160	0.253
1/0	105600	19	0.074	0.373	0.109	0.122	0.127	0.201
2/0	133100	19	0.084	0.419	0.138	0.0967	0.101	0.159
3/0	167800	19	0.094	0.470	0.173	0.0766	0.0797	0.126
4/0	211600	19	0.106	0.528	0.219	0.0608	0.0626	0.100
250	—	37	0.082	0.575	0.260	0.0515	0.0535	0.0847
300	—	37	0.090	0.630	0.312	0.0429	0.0446	0.0707
350	—	37	0.097	0.681	0.364	0.0367	0.0382	0.0605
400	—	37	0.104	0.728	0.416	0.0321	0.0331	0.0529
500	—	37	0.116	0.813	0.519	0.0258	0.0265	0.0424
600	—	61	0.992	0.893	0.626	0.0214	0.0223	0.0353
700	—	61	0.107	0.964	0.730	0.0184	0.0189	0.0303
750	—	61	0.111	0.998	0.782	0.0171	0.0176	0.0282
800	—	61	0.114	1.03	0.834	0.0161	0.0166	0.0265
900	—	61	0.122	1.09	0.940	0.0143	0.0147	0.0235
1000	—	61	0.128	1.15	1.04	0.0129	0.0132	0.0212
1250	—	91	0.117	1.29	1.30	0.0103	0.0106	0.0169
1500	—	91	0.128	1.41	1.57	0.00858	0.00883	0.0141
1750	—	127	0.117	1.52	1.83	0.00735	0.00735	0.0121
2000	—	127	0.126	1.63	2.09	0.00643	0.00662	0.0106

These resistance values are valid ONLY for the parameters as given. Using conductors having coated strands, different stranding type, and especially, other temperatures, change the resistance.

Formula for temperature change: $R_2 = R_1 [1 + \alpha(T_2 - 75)]$ where: $\alpha_{cu} = 0.00323$, $\alpha_{al} = 0.00330$.

Conductors with compact and compressed stranding have about 9 percent and 3 percent, respectively, smaller bare conductor diameters than those shown. See Table 5A for actual compact cable dimensions.

The IACS conductivities used: bare copper = 100%, aluminum = 61%.

Class B stranding is listed as well as solid for some sizes. Its overall diameter and area is that of its circumscribing circle.

(FPN): The construction information is per NEMA WC8-1976 (Rev 5-1980). The resistance is calculated per National Bureau of Standards Handbook 100, dated 1966, and Handbook 109, dated 1972.

The notes below Table 8 state: These resistance values are valid **only** for the parameters (measures) given. The resistance values are shown at 75°C.

The notes show a formula for temperature change with the coefficient of 0.00323 for copper and a coefficient of 0.00330 for aluminum. **Coefficient** is a number that serves as a measure; the proportion that resistance changes per degree rise in temperature is called the temperature coefficient of resistance.

With a 15°C change in temperature from 75°C to 90°C, using the formula for temperature change, for copper 15° x 0.00323 = .04845 + 1 = 1.04845 or a factor of **1.05** for a 15° change.

For aluminum a 15° change is 15° x 0.00330 = .0495 + 1 = 1.0495 or a factor of **1.05** for aluminum for a 15° change.

FOR 15° C CHANGE
1.05 FACTOR

Example: Table 8 shows a #6 uncoated copper resistance of .491 ohm per k/ft @ 75°C. If using a #6, 90°C conductor, the resistance would have to be **increased** by the 1.05 factor for a 15° change = .491 x 1.05 =**.51555 ohm resistance**.

If using a #6, 60°C conductor, the resistance can be **decreased** by the 1.05 factor for a 15° change = .491/1.05 = **.467619 ohm resistance**.

Since the 1984 Code, voltage drop is concerning both the **size** and the **temperature**.

As shown above, one conductor size can have **three** resistance values, depending on the temperature (insulation rating).

#6 THW = .491 ohms per k/ft

#6 THHN = .51555 ohms per k/ft

#6 TW = .467619 ohms per k/ft

THW = 75°C - 167°F

THHN = 90°C - 194°F

TW = 60°C - 140°F

When calculating resistance values, start with Table 8 resistance for 75°C. For an **increase** in temperature to 90°C simply **multiply** the 75°C value by 1.05. For a **decrease** in temperature to 60°C **divide** the 75°C value by 1.05.

NOTE...

Table resistance values are based on 75°C - 167°F

The exact K factor also changes with a temperature change:

At 75°C $\longrightarrow$ Exact K $= \dfrac{R \ x \ CM}{1000 \ Feet}$

At 90°C $\longrightarrow$ Exact K $= \dfrac{R \ x \ CM \ x \ 1.05}{1000 \ Feet}$

At 60°C $\longrightarrow$ Exact K $= \dfrac{R \ x \ CM}{1000 \ Feet \ x \ 1.05}$

On the following page is a table for the exact K at 75°C that I designed. These values shown in the table would be **multiplied** by the 1.05 factor for a 90°C conductor to find the exact K. For a 60°C conductor the values shown in the table would be **divided** by the 1.05 factor.

Example: What is the exact K factor of a #6 THHN uncoated copper conductor?

Solution: Table for exact K @ 75°C shows 12.88384 x 1.05 = **13.528032 exact K @ 90°C**.

Example: What is the exact K for a #4 TW aluminum conductor?

Solution: Table for exact K @ 75°C shows 21.20392/1.05 = **20.194209 exact K @ 60°C**.

EXACT K @ 75°C

DESIGNED BY TOM HENRY
CODE ELECTRICAL CLASSES

AWG	Area Circular Mils	Copper Un-coated Resistance	Copper Un-coated EXACT K	Copper Coated Resistance	Copper Coated EXACT K	Aluminum Resistance	Aluminum EXACT K
#14 SOLID	4110	3.07	12.6177	3.19	13.1109	5.06	20.7966
#14 STRANDED	4110	3.14	12.9054	3.26	13.3986	5.17	21.2487
#12 SOLID	6530	1.93	12.6029	2.01	13.1253	3.18	20.7654
#12 STRANDED	6530	1.98	12.9294	2.05	13.3865	3.25	21.2225
#10 SOLID	10 380	1.21	12.5598	1.26	13.0788	2.00	20.76
#10 STRANDED	10 380	1.24	12.8712	1.29	13.3902	2.04	21.1752
#8 SOLID	16 510	0.764	12.61364	0.786	12.97686	1.26	20.8026
#8 STRANDED	16 510	0.778	12.84478	0.809	13.35659	1.28	21.1328
#6	26 240	0.491	12.88384	0.510	13.3824	0.808	21.20192
#4	41 740	0.308	12.85592	0.321	13.39854	0.508	21.20392
#3	52 620	0.245	12.8919	0.254	13.36548	0.403	21.20586
#2	66 360	0.194	12.87384	0.201	13.33836	0.319	21.16884
#1	83 690	0.154	12.88826	0.160	13.3904	0.253	21.17357
#1/0	105 600	0.122	12.8832	0.127	13.4112	0.201	21.2256
#2/0	133 100	0.0967	12.87077	0.101	13.4431	0.159	21.1629
#3/0	167 800	0.0766	12.85348	0.0797	13.37366	0.126	21.1428
#4/0	211 600	0.0608	12.86528	0.0626	13.24616	0.100	21.16
250 kcmil	250 000	0.0515	12.875	0.0535	13.375	0.0847	21.175
500 kcmil	500 000	0.0258	12.9	0.0265	13.25	0.0424	21.2
1000 kcmil	1 000 000	0.0129	12.9	0.0132	13.2	0.0212	21.2

So far we have been calculating voltage drop using the resistance values from Table 8.

Table 8 is DC resistance values. In a DC circuit, current flows throughout the diameter of the conductor in a uniform density.

An AC circuit has some factors that don't affect a DC circuit such as skin effect, inductive reactance, capacity of a circuit and power factor of the load.

With conductors #250 kcmil and larger in an AC circuit, the skin effect becomes a higher resistance factor as the current does not flow uniformly as in a DC circuit but is more on the **skin** of the conductor.

DENSITY

DC   **AC**

In the 1981 Code, Table 9 was simply a multiply factor to calculate the AC resistance from Table 8 values for conductors larger than #4/0.

Now Table 9 in the Code shows the AC resistance values per k/ft @ 75°C, incorporating the skin effect factor in the larger conductors.

Table 9 shows the AC resistance for uncoated copper in PVC conduit, in aluminum conduit, and in steel conduit. Table 9 also shows the resistance for aluminum wires in the different raceways.

Table 9. AC Resistance and Reactance for 600 V cables, 3 phase 60, Hz, 75°C (167°F) — Three Single Conductors in Conduit

Size AWG/ kcmil	X (Inductance) for All Wires		AC Resistance for Uncoated Copper Wires			AC Resistance for Aluminum Wires			Effective Z at .85 PF for Uncoated Copper Wires			Effective Z at .85 PF for Aluminum Wires			Size AWG/ MCM
	PVC, Al. Conduits	Steel Conduit	PVC Conduit	Al. Conduit	Steel Conduit	PVC Conduit	Al. Conduit	Steel Conduit	PVC Conduit	Al. Conduit	Steel Conduit	PVC Conduit	Al. Conduit	Steel Conduit	
14	.058	.073	3.1	3.1	3.1	—	—	—	2.7	2.7	2.7	—	—	—	14
12	.054	.068	2.0	2.0	2.0	3.2	3.2	3.2	1.7	1.7	1.7	2.8	2.8	2.8	12
10	.050	.063	1.2	1.2	1.2	2.0	2.0	2.0	1.1	1.1	1.1	1.8	1.8	1.8	10
8	.052	.065	0.78	0.78	0.78	1.3	1.3	1.3	0.69	0.69	0.70	1.1	1.1	1.1	8
6	.051	.064	0.49	0.49	0.49	0.81	0.81	0.81	0.44	0.045	0.45	0.71	0.72	0.72	6
4	.048	.060	0.31	0.31	0.31	0.51	0.51	0.51	0.29	0.29	0.30	0.46	0.46	0.46	4
3	.047	.059	0.25	0.25	0.25	0.40	0.41	0.40	0.23	0.24	0.24	0.37	0.37	0.37	3
2	.045	.057	0.19	0.20	0.20	0.32	0.32	0.32	0.19	0.19	0.20	0.30	0.30	0.30	2
1	.046	.057	0.15	0.16	0.16	0.25	0.26	0.25	0.16	0.16	0.16	0.24	0.24	0.25	1
1/0	.044	.055	0.12	0.13	0.12	0.20	0.21	0.20	0.13	0.13	0.13	0.19	0.20	0.20	1/0
2/0	.043	.054	0.10	0.10	0.10	0.16	0.16	0.16	0.11	0.11	0.11	0.16	0.16	0.16	2/0
3/0	.042	.052	0.077	0.082	0.079	0.13	0.13	0.13	0.088	0.092	0.094	0.13	0.13	0.14	3/0
4/0	.041	.051	0.062	0.067	0.063	0.10	0.11	0.10	0.074	0.078	0.080	0.11	0.11	0.11	4/0
250	.041	.052	0.052	0.057	0.054	0.085	0.090	0.086	0.056	0.070	0.073	0.094	0.098	0.10	250
300	.041	.051	0.044	0.049	0.045	0.071	0.076	0.072	0.059	0.063	0.065	0.082	0.086	0.088	300
350	.040	.050	0.038	0.043	0.039	0.061	0.066	0.063	0.053	0.058	0.060	0.073	0.077	0.080	350
400	.040	.049	0.033	0.038	0.035	0.054	0.059	0.055	0.049	0.053	0.056	0.066	0.071	0.073	400
500	.039	.048	0.027	0.032	0.029	0.043	0.048	0.045	0.043	0.048	0.050	0.057	0.061	0.064	500
600	.039	.048	0.023	0.028	0.025	0.036	0.041	0.038	0.040	0.044	0.047	0.051	0.055	0.058	600
750	.038	.048	0.019	0.024	0.021	0.029	0.034	0.031	0.036	0.040	0.043	0.045	0.049	0.052	750
1000	.037	.046	0.015	0.019	0.018	0.023	0.027	0.025	0.032	0.036	0.040	0.039	0.042	0.046	1000

Ohms to neutral per 1000 feet

Notes:

1. These values are based on the following constants: UL-type RHH wires with Class B stranding, in cradles configuration. Wire conductivities are 100% IACS copper, and 61% IACS aluminum, and aluminum onduit is 45% IACS. Capacitive reactance is ignored since it is negligible at these voltages.
These resistance values are valid only at 75°C (167°F) and for the parameters as given, but are representative for 600-volt wire types operating at 60 Hz.

2. "Effective Z" is defined as $R^x \cos(\text{theta}) + X^x \sin(\text{theta})$, where "theta" is the power factor angle of the circuit. Multiplying current by effective impedance gives a good approximation for line to neutral voltage drop. Effective impedance values shown in this table are valid only at .85 power factor.
For another circuit power factor (PF), effective impedance(Ze) can be calculated from R and X values given in this table as follows:
$Ze = R^x \, PF + X^x \sin[\arccos(PF)]$

Table 8. Conductor Properties

Size AWG / kcmil	Area Circ. Mils	Stranding Quantity	Stranding Diam. In.	Overall Diam. In.	Overall Area In.²	Copper Uncoated ohm / kFT	Copper Coated ohm / kFT	Aluminum ohm / kFT
18	1620	1	—	0.040	0.001	7.77	8.08	12.8
18	1620	7	0.015	0.046	0.002	7.95	8.45	13.1
16	2580	1	—	0.051	0.002	4.89	5.08	8.05
16	2580	7	0.019	0.058	0.003	4.99	5.29	8.21
14	4110	1	—	0.064	0.003	3.07	3.19	5.06
14	4110	7	0.024	0.073	0.004	3.14	3.26	5.17
12	6530	1	—	0.081	0.005	1.93	2.01	3.18
12	6530	7	0.030	0.092	0.006	1.98	2.05	3.25
10	10380	1	—	0.102	0.008	1.21	1.26	2.00
10	10380	7	0.038	0.116	0.011	1.24	1.29	2.04
8	16510	1	—	0.128	0.013	0.764	0.786	1.26
8	16510	7	0.049	0.146	0.017	0.778	0.809	1.28
6	26240	7	0.061	0.184	0.027	0.491	0.510	0.808
4	41740	7	0.077	0.232	0.042	0.308	0.321	0.508
3	52620	7	0.087	0.260	0.053	0.245	0.254	0.403
2	66360	7	0.097	0.292	0.067	0.194	0.201	0.319
1	83690	19	0.066	0.332	0.087	0.154	0.160	0.253
1/0	105600	19	0.074	0.373	0.109	0.122	0.127	0.201
2/0	133100	19	0.084	0.419	0.138	0.0967	0.101	0.159
3/0	167800	19	0.094	0.470	0.173	0.0766	0.0797	0.126
4/0	211600	19	0.106	0.528	0.219	0.0608	0.0626	0.100
250	—	37	0.082	0.575	0.260	0.0515	0.0535	0.0847
300	—	37	0.090	0.630	0.312	0.0429	0.0446	0.0707
350	—	37	0.097	0.681	0.364	0.0367	0.0382	0.0605
400	—	37	0.104	0.728	0.416	0.0321	0.0331	0.0529
500	—	37	0.116	0.813	0.519	0.0258	0.0265	0.0424
600	—	61	0.992	0.893	0.626	0.0214	0.0223	0.0353
700	—	61	0.107	0.964	0.730	0.0184	0.0189	0.0303
750	—	61	0.111	0.998	0.782	0.0171	0.0176	0.0282
800	—	61	0.114	1.03	0.834	0.0161	0.0166	0.0265
900	—	61	0.122	1.09	0.940	0.0143	0.0147	0.0235
1000	—	61	0.128	1.15	1.04	0.0129	0.0132	0.0212
1250	—	91	0.117	1.29	1.30	0.0103	0.0106	0.0169
1500	—	91	0.128	1.41	1.57	0.00858	0.00883	0.0141
1750	—	127	0.117	1.52	1.83	0.00735	0.00735	0.0121
2000	—	127	0.126	1.63	2.09	0.00643	0.00662	0.0106

Table 9. AC Resistance

Size AWG/ kcmil	X (Inductance) for All Wires PVC, Al. Conduits	X (Inductance) for All Wires Steel Conduit	AC Resistance for Uncoated Copper Wires PVC Conduit	AC Resistance for Uncoated Copper Wires Al. Conduit	AC Resistance for Uncoated Copper Wires Steel Conduit
14	.058	.073	3.1	3.1	3.1
12	.054	.068	2.0	2.0	2.0
10	.050	.063	1.2	1.2	1.2
8	.052	.065	0.78	0.78	0.78
6	.051	.064	0.49	0.49	0.49
4	.048	.060	0.31	0.31	0.31
3	.047	.059	0.25	0.25	0.25
2	.045	.057	0.19	0.20	0.20
1	.046	.057	0.15	0.16	0.16
1/0	.044	.055	0.12	0.13	0.12
2/0	.043	.054	0.10	0.10	0.10
3/0	.042	.052	0.077	0.082	0.079
4/0	.041	.051	0.062	0.067	0.063
250	.041	.052	0.052	0.057	0.054
300	.041	.051	0.044	0.049	0.045
350	.040	.050	0.038	0.043	0.039
400	.040	.049	0.033	0.038	0.035
500	.039	.048	0.027	0.032	0.029
600	.039	.048	0.023	0.028	0.025
750	.038	.048	0.019	0.024	0.021
1000	.037	.046	0.015	0.019	0.018

Table 8 shows a #6 uncoated copper at .491 ohms per k/ft.

Table 9 shows a #6 uncoated copper at .49 ohms per k/ft.

There is very little difference between the two tables. Table 8 shows the DC conductor with a slightly higher resistance than the AC conductor from Table 9.

Table 8 DC resistance shows a #250 kcmil copper at .0515 ohms per k/ft and Table 9 AC resistance shows a #250 kcmil copper in steel conduit at .054 ohms per k/ft, a higher resistance than DC.

Larger size conductors from Table 9 AC resistance will reflect even more how important it is to use the **exact K** factor when calculating voltage drop calculations.

Example: Using Table 9, find the exact K for a #1000 kcmil 90°C rated **copper** conductor in a steel conduit.

Solution: Exact K = $\dfrac{.018\Omega \times 1,000,000\text{cm} \times 1.05}{1000 \text{ feet}}$ = **18.9 exact K for copper @ 90°C**.

The factors in an AC circuit that don't affect a DC circuit can be **neglected** in the smaller AC conductors up to #250 kcmil.

In this book use **Table 8** to find resistance values of conductors unless Table 9 is specified.

A branch circuit with several loads is a more complex voltage drop calculation than a branch circuit with only one load.

Example: Using a #12 THW uncoated stranded copper conductor, calculate the voltage drop in the following branch circuit with three 4 amp loads.

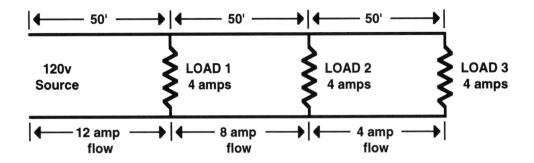

STEP ONE: Find the voltage drop between the 120v source and LOAD 1.

VD = I x R

I = 12 amp current flow in the conductors

Table 8, #12 = 1.98 ohms per k/ft x .100 feet = .198 ohm

VD = 12 amps x .198 ohm = 2.376 volts dropped from the source to LOAD 1

STEP TWO: Find the voltage drop between LOAD 1 and LOAD 2

VD = I x R

I = 8 amp current flow in the conductors

VD = 8 amps x .198 ohm = 1.584 volts dropped from LOAD 1 to LOAD 2

STEP THREE: Find the voltage drop between LOAD 2 and LOAD 3

VD = I x R

I = 4 amp current flow in the conductors

VD = 4 amps x .198 ohm = .792 volts dropped from LOAD 2 to LOAD 3

The **total voltage drop** = 2.376v + 1.584v + .792v = **4.752 total voltage drop**

This is **more** voltage drop than the Code recommends. The Code recommends 3% of 120 volts which is **3.6** volts dropped maximum permitted.

Example: The following diagram shows eight parking lot lights at 2 amp each. Four of the lights are wired with a #10 stranded uncoated conductor; three of the lights are wired with a #8 stranded uncoated conductor. What size conductor is required from the 240v single-phase source to the first light 200 feet in distance?

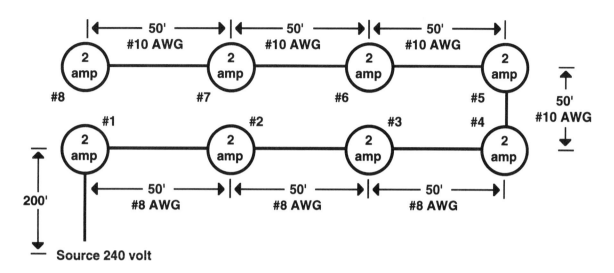

Solution: The Code allows a VD of 3% of 240v = 7.2 volts. First you must find the voltage drop between the lights to determine how many volts **are left** to drop in the 200 feet to the source. There is 100 feet of conductor between each of the lights, use Table 8.

VOLTAGE DROP BETWEEN LIGHTS

#8 - #7 #10 resistance = .124 ohm x 2 amp = .248   volts dropped
#7 - #6 #10 resistance = .124 ohm x 4 amp = .496   volts dropped
#6 - #5 #10 resistance = .124 ohm x 6 amp = .744   volts dropped
#5 - #4 #10 resistance = .124 ohm x 8 amp = .992   volts dropped
#4 - #3 #8   resistance = .0778 ohm x 10 amp = .778   volts dropped
#3 - #2 #8   resistance = .0778 ohm x 12 amp = .9336 volts dropped
#2 - #1 #8   resistance = .0778 ohm x 14 amp = **1.0892 volts dropped**
                                                5.2808 volts dropped

 7.2 total voltage drop permitted
-5.2808 volts dropped between the lights
 1.9192 volts **left to drop** in this branch circuit

Now you are ready to calculate the conductor required between the source and the first light.

$$CM = \frac{2 \times 12.9 \times 200 \text{ feet} \times 16 \text{ amp}}{1.9192 \text{ volts left to drop}} = 43{,}017.9 \text{ CM required}$$

Table 8: #3 conductor has a cma of 52,620

Answer: **#3 conductor**

Summary: Excessive voltage drop causes problems such as the overheating of motors, appliances not operating properly, insufficient lighting, etc. Low voltage on a circular handsaw can cause dangerous "kickback" of the blade.

It is impossible to eliminate voltage drop **completely** because of the resistance in the conductors to the load. But we have learned how to **lower** the voltage drop.

Voltage drop is **wasted** power (watts). The **Code recommendation** to limit voltage drop to 3% on branch circuits and 5% total is very **inefficient**.

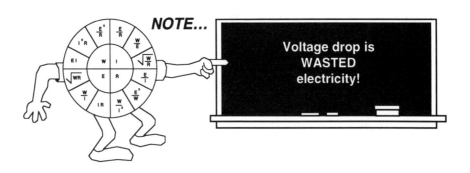

NOTE...

Voltage drop is
WASTED
electricity!

CALCULATING VOLTAGE DROP COST

What does excessive voltage drop cost?

Example: What size conductor is required to meet the Code recommendation of 3% voltage drop?

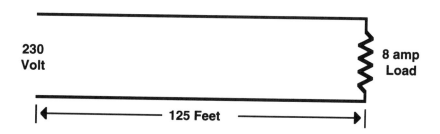

Solution: $CM = \dfrac{2 \times 12.9 \times 125 \text{ feet} \times 8 \text{ amp}}{6.9 \text{ voltage drop permitted}} = 3739 \text{ CM required}$

Table 8: #14 conductor has 4110 CM

What is the actual voltage drop using a #14 conductor?

$VD = I \times R$

$I = 8$ amps

Table 8: #14 stranded uncoated = 3.14 ohm x .250 feet = .785 ohm

$VD = 8$ amps x .785 ohm = **6.28 volts dropped**

Power Loss = VD x I   6.28v x 8 amps = **50.24 watt loss**

Cost of power loss based on a 30 day month load operating 12 hours each day; electricity cost based on .07 cents per kwh (kilowatt hour).

$\dfrac{50 \text{ watt} \times 12 \text{ hours} \times 30 \text{ days} \times .07 \text{ kwh}}{1000}$ = **$1.26 cost per month for wasted power**

Now instead of using a #14 conductor, use a #12 conductor and **compare the cost**.

Find the actual voltage drop using a #12 stranded uncoated copper conductor.
VD = I x R
Table 8: #12 = 1.98 ohms per k/ft x .250 feet = .495 ohm
VD = 8 amps x .495 ohm = 3.96 volts dropped
Power Loss = VD x I = 3.96 volts x 8 amps = 31.68 watt loss
Cost = 32 watts x 12 hours x 30 days x .07 kwh = **81¢ cost per month for wasted power**

Using a #12 conductor instead of a #14 conductor results in a monthly savings of 45¢ or $5.40 a year in savings. And remember, this is an increase of one wire size for only one load. This example could have been your swimming pool filtration pump motor.

Example: What size conductor is required to meet the Code recommendation for the branch circuit shown below?

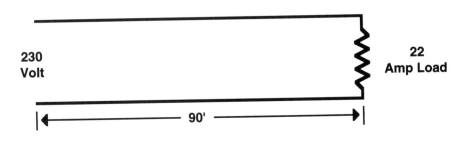

**230
Volt**

**22
Amp Load**

90'

CM = $\dfrac{2 \times 12.9 \times 90 \text{ feet} \times 22 \text{ amps}}{6.9 \text{ vd permitted}}$ = 7403 cm required

Table 8: #10 has 10380 cm

What is the actual voltage drop using a #10 conductor?
VD = I x R
Table 8: #10 stranded uncoated = 1.24 ohms x .180 feet = .2232 ohm
VD = 22 amps x .2232 ohm = 4.9104 volts dropped
Power Loss = VD x I = 4.9104v x 22 amps = 108 watts wasted power
Cost = 108 x 12 hours x 30 days x .07 kwh = **$2.72 per month wasted power**

Now instead of using a #10 conductor, select a **larger** conductor, a #4 and **compare** the cost for wasted electricity.

VD = I x R
Table 8: #4 = .308 ohm per k/ft x .180 feet = .05544 ohm
VD = 22 amps x .05544 ohm = 1.21968 volts dropped
Power Loss = VD x I = 1.21968v x 22 amps = 26.8 watt wasted power
Cost = 26.8 watt x 12 hours x 30 days x .07 kwh = **.68¢ cost per month wasted power**

By using a #4 conductor instead of the minimum #10 required by the Code, results in a monthly savings of $2.72 - .68 = **$2.04 per month** or a yearly savings of **$24.48**.

This 22 amp load could be the 3 ton air-conditioning unit in your house.

Now you should have a better understanding of voltage drop.

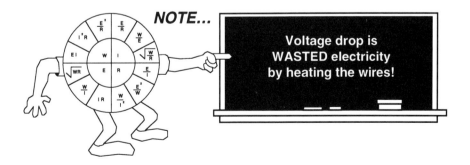

NOTE...

Voltage drop is
WASTED electricity
by heating the wires!

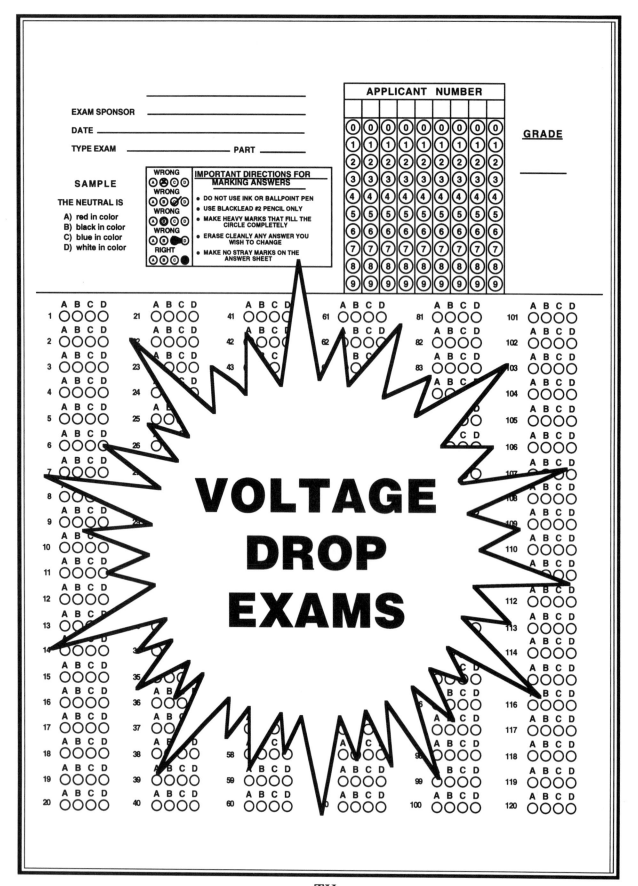

1. The voltage drop on two #12 solid uncoated THW conductors, 150 feet long, connecting a 9.8 amp load to a 115 volt source would be ____ volts.

(a) 3.45   (b) 5.75   (c) 5.6742   (d) none of these

2. What is the the voltage drop on a branch circuit to a load of 11 amps located 175 feet from the 208 volt single-phase source using #8 THW stranded copper conductors?

(a) 2.9414 volts   (b) 2.9953 volts   (c) 3.008 volts   (d) none of these

3. What size THW conductor is required for a 208 volt, 3 ø branch circuit that has a 15 amp load located 180 feet from the source?

(a) #14   (b) #12   (c) #10   (d) #8

4. How far from a single-phase 240 volt source can you install #10 THW stranded copper conductors if the load is 16 amps on the branch circuit?

(a) 90.52 feet   (b) 181.45 feet   (c) 209.52 feet   (d) 315.6 feet

5. What is the maximum load permitted on a 115 volt single-phase branch circuit using #12 THW stranded conductors 150 feet from the source?

(a) 6.06 amps   (b) 5.08 amps   (c) 4.69 amps   (d) 5.80 amps

6. What size conductor for a 1 ø, 1 1/2 hp, 230 volt motor with a full-load current of 10 amps, 150 feet from the source?

(a) #14 THW cu   (b) #12 THW cu   (c) #10 THW cu   (d) #8 THW cu

7. What is the voltage drop in a branch circuit to an 11 amp load, the load is located 175 feet from a 208v 1 ø source using #8 solid AL conductors?

(a) 2.9414 volts   (b) 2.9953 volts   (c) 4.928 volts   (d) 4.851 volts

1. The circuit load is 100 amps. What is the voltage at the load?

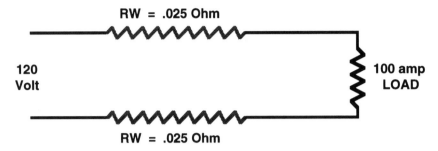

RW = .025 Ohm

**120
Volt**

**100 amp
LOAD**

RW = .025 Ohm

(a) 115 volts   (b) 115.4 volts   (c) 117.5 volts   (d) 120 volts

2. What size aluminum THW conductor is required to a 60 amp branch circuit , 148 feet from the 240 volt single-phase source?

(a) #4   (b) #3   (c) #2   (d) #1

3. Two #12 solid uncoated copper wires are shorted. When 12 volts are applied, a current of 20 amps develops. What is the approximate distance from the supply to the short?

(a) 300 - 310 feet   (b) 150 - 160 feet   (c) 420 - 430 feet   (d) 40 -50 feet

4. A 2 ohm resistor is connected in series with a 20 ohm lamp in series with a 1 ohm resistor. If the voltage drop across the 1 ohm resistor is 5 volts, the source voltage will be _____ volts.

(a) 560   (b) 115   (c) 110   (d) 150

5. If the source voltage is 120 volts and the sub-panel voltage is 116.5 volts, what is the voltage the Code recommends at the load?

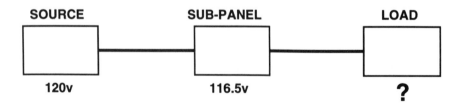

SOURCE   **SUB-PANEL**   **LOAD**

120v   **116.5v**   **?**

(a) 113 volts   (b) 114 volts   (c) 115 volts   (d) 116 volts

1. A #6 RHW uncoated copper conductor has a total resistance of .05 ohm. What is the approximate length of this conductor?

(a) 102 feet   (b) 108 feet   (c) 96 feet   (d) 150 feet

2. What is the resistance per phase of the conductors feeding a 3 ø, 230 volt, 20 hp motor from a 230 volt branch circuit panel? Use THW stranded copper uncoated and a 3% voltage drop.

(a) 0.1278 ohm   (b) 0.074 ohm   (c) 0.308 ohm   (d) 0.4091 ohm

3. At 3% voltage drop, how far is the load from the source, using a #6 THW?

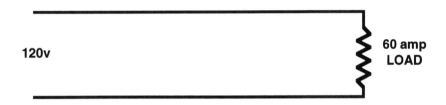

(a) 30 feet   (b) 34.6 feet   (c) 61 feet   (d) 72.4 feet

4. What is the resistance of 85 feet of #2, 90°C rated insulation, uncoated copper conductor?

(a) .0173145 ohm   (b) .1649 ohm   (c) .194 ohm   (d) .173145 ohm

5. What size THW conductor is required for a 208 volt three-phase branch circuit that has a 15 amp load located 126 feet from the source?

(a) #12   (b) #10   (c) #8   (d) #6

6. Two #6 THW aluminum conductors in a branch circuit to a 50 amp load; the source voltage is 120. With 3% voltage drop, find the total length of the conductors.

(a) 30 - 40 feet   (b) 41 - 50   (c) 51 - 75 feet   (d) 76 - 90 feet

1. What is the resistance of 167 feet of #2 aluminum conductor?

(a) .032 ohm   (b) .053 ohm   (c) .033 ohm   (d) .319 ohm

2. How far from a three-phase 208 volt source can you install #4 THW uncoated copper conductors, if the branch circuit load is 45 amps?

(a) 129 feet   (b) 224.3 feet   (c) 225.1 feet   (d) 259.9 feet

3. Parallel, #500 kcmil THW uncoated copper conductors for 250 feet. What is the total resistance?

(a) .0129 ohm   (b) .0064 ohm   (c) .0032 ohm   (d) .0258 ohm

4. What is the maximum load permitted on a 220 volt, three-phase, #10 RHW stranded uncoated copper conductor 160 feet from the source?

(a) 16.63 amps   (b) 17.38 amps   (c) 19.2 amps   (d) 23 amps

5. In the following branch circuit, what is the voltage at the load?

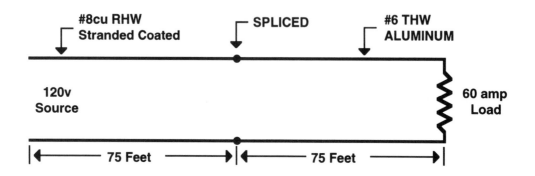

(a) 100 volts   (b) 108 volts   (c) 105.5 volts   (d) 112 volts

1. Find the approximate distance between the source and the load if a #6 THW conductor is used and the total conductor resistance is .04 ohm.

(a) 41 feet   (b) 94 feet   (c) 82 feet   (d) 105 feet

2. What size aluminum conductor is required for the 150 feet between the junction box and the load?

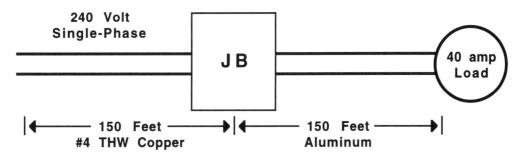

(a) #1   (b) #2   (c) #3   (d) #4

3. What is the maximum load permitted on a 120 volt, single-phase branch circuit, using a #14 THW stranded uncoated copper conductor, 100 feet from the source?

(a) 3.48 amps   (b) 5.73 amps   (c) 6.62 amps   (d) 8.14 amps

4. What is the voltage drop in a branch circuit to a 1 1/2 hp 208 volt single-phase motor? The motor is located 175 feet from the source using #8 THW stranded aluminum conductors.

(a) 3 volts   (b) 4.49 volts   (c) 4.928 volts   (d) 6.12 volts

5. How far from a single-phase 240 volt source can you install a #10 THW stranded uncoated copper conductor if the load is 16 amps? Use 3% VD.

(a) 90 feet   (b) 125 feet   (c) 181 feet   (d) 209 feet

6. What is the Table 9 AC resistance of 500 feet of #8 RHW in metal conduit?

(a) 0.78 ohm   (b) 0.39 ohm   (c) 0.195 ohm   (d) 0.0975 ohm

1.

**240 Volt
Single-Phase**

I. What is the minimum size THW stranded uncoated copper feeder conductor permitted?

(a) #10   (b) #8   (c) #6   (d) #4

II. What is the actual **total** voltage drop?

(a) 9.72 volts   (b) 10.86 volts   (c) 11.76 volts   (d) 12 volts

2.

   If the source voltage at the main panel is 240 volts, the Code recommends a minimum of _____ volts at the load.

(a) 237.6   (b) 235.2   (c) 232.8   (d) 228

3. Find the recommended conductor size as per NEC for a 230v single-phase 7 1/2 hp motor, 350 feet from its three-phase source.

(a) #0 THW   (b) #8 THW   (c) #3 THW   (d) #400 kcmil THW

4. If the source voltage is 120v on the branch circuit, the load is 6000w, 200 feet from the source, the size of conductor should be a # _____ THW.

(a) 3   (b) 2   (c) 1   (d) 1/0

1. The maximum permitted voltage drop is ____ volts on a 240v branch circuit.

(a) 12 (b) 1.2 (c) 0.72 (d) 7.2

2. If a 115 volt source has a 3 volt drop to the load, what is the percent of voltage drop?

(a) 2.6% (b) 2.68% (c) 3% (d) 4%

3. What size copper conductor is required for a 12 amp load, 225 feet from a 120 volt single-phase source?

(a) #12 THW (b) #10 THW (c) #8 THW (d) #6 THW

4. If the branch circuit source voltage is 115 volts and the load voltage is 112 volts, what distance is the 45 amp single-phase load from the branch circuit panel? Use THW solid copper uncoated.

(a) 50 to 60 feet (b) 61 to 70 feet (c) 80 to 90 feet (d) none of these

5. Given: Source 3 ø 208 volt, load is 360 kva on 3 ø 208v, 200 feet from the source. The size conductor needed for the above load is a ____ THW copper.

(a) #750 kcmil (b) #900 kcmil (c) #1056 kcmil (d) none of these

6. The AC resistance of 1000 feet of #500 kcmil copper uncoated in a non-metallic conduit is larger than the DC resistance on the same conductor by ____ ohms.

(a) .0258 (b) .036 (c) .0012 (d) .0102

7. The total resistance of two #12 solid uncoated copper THW conductors, in parallel, each 150' long, is approximately ____ ohms.

(a) 0.14475 (b) 0.2895 (c) 0.579 (d) 1.93

1. The voltage drop on two #12 stranded, uncoated THW conductors, 100 ft. long, connecting a 1 hp, 1ø 115V motor to a 115-volt source, would be _____ volts.

(a) 3.4500   (b) 5.75   (c) 6.336   (d) 6.530

2. Find the approximate length of one of the conductors used between the service and the load if a #6 THW uncoated Cu conductor is used and the conductor resistance is 0.035.

(a) 28.57   (b) 36   (c) 71   (d) 107

THE NEXT TWO QUESTIONS REFER TO THE DIAGRAM

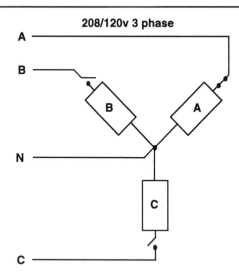

208/120v 3 phase

3. If load A is 12 KVA, and the conductor size is #1 THW copper, how far from the source can the load A be located and not exceed 3% voltage drop?

(a) 100 feet   (b) 116 feet   (c) 195 feet   (d) 202 feet

4. What would be the voltage drop if the #1 THW copper conductor is supplying a 12 KVA load A, 116 feet from the source?

(a) 5 volts   (b) 3.58 volts   (c) 3 volts   (d) 2.86 volts

5. At no load the terminal voltage of an alternator is 530 volts. At rated load, the voltage drops to 480 volts. The percent of voltage drop is _____.

(a) 9.43%   (b) 10.42%   (c) 12.52 %   (d) 15%

VOLTAGE DROP EXAM #9

1. The source voltage is 208V 3ø. The load is 120 kVA on 3ø 208V -- 100 feet from the source. The size conductor when installed in a conduit should be a _____ Cu THW.

(a) 2/0 AWG   (b) 3/0 AWG   (c) 300 kcmil   (d) 400 kcmil

2. In the sketch shown below, if load A is 9.6 kVA and the conductor size is a #3 THW copper, how far from the source can the load A be located and not exceed 3% voltage drop?

(a) 159 feet   (b) 125 feet   (c) 91.8 feet   (d) 90 feet

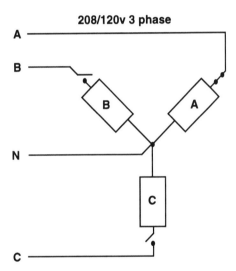

208/120v 3 phase

3. The voltage at the service is 118 volts. A 60-amp subpanel feed with a #6 THW is 60 feet away from the main panel. From there it is 150 feet to a 11.5 amp. 1 ø, 115V, 3/4 hp motor. What size conductor is recommended to satisfactorily operate this motor?

(a) #12   (b) #10   (c) #6   (d) #4

4. The source voltage is 480 volts, the load current at 460 volts is 16 amps, distance from source to load is 2,500 feet. What is the resistance of the conductors feeding this load?

(a) 0.75Ω   (b) 1.25Ω   (c) 2.50Ω   (d) 5.00Ω

EXAM SPONSOR _____

DATE _____

TYPE EXAM _____ PART _____

SAMPLE

THE NEUTRAL IS

A) red in color
B) black in color
C) blue in color
D) white in color

WRONG
WRONG
WRONG
WRONG
RIGHT

IMPORTANT DIRECTIONS FOR MARKING ANSWERS

- DO NOT USE INK OR BALLPOINT PEN
- USE BLACKLEAD #2 PENCIL ONLY
- MAKE HEAVY MARKS THAT FILL THE CIRCLE COMPLETELY
- ERASE CLEANLY ANY ANSWER YOU WISH TO CHANGE
- MAKE NO STRAY MARKS ON THE ANSWER SHEET

APPLICANT NUMBER

GRADE

FINAL EXAM #1

FINAL EXAM #1

1. The circuit shown below has a total resistance of 8 ohms. The resistance of R2 would be _____ Ω.

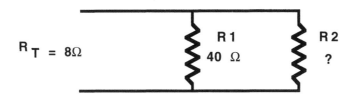

(a) 5   (b) 8   (c) 10   (d) 48

2. In the circuit shown below, the current flow is _____.

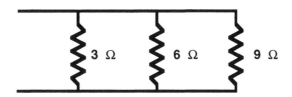

(a) equal in all three resistors   (b) highest through the 9Ω resistor
(c) lowest through the 3Ω resistor   (d) highest through the 3Ω resistor

3. In the circuit shown below, the ammeter would read _____ amps.

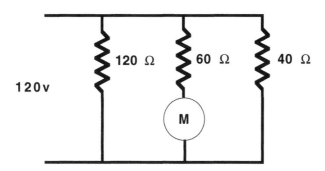

(a) 2   (b) 6   (c) 60   (d) .545

4. The total current flowing in the circuit above would be _____ amps.

(a) 2   (b) 6   (c) 60   (d) .545

5. In the circuit shown below, the source voltage would be ____ volts.

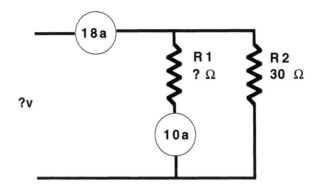

(a) 58   (b) 120   (c) 90   (d) 240

6. The resistance of R1 in the circuit shown above would be approximately ____ ohms.

(a) 24   (b) 15   (c) 8   (d) 12

7. In the circuit shown below all three resistors have the same ohmic value, the resistance of R2 would be ____ ohms.

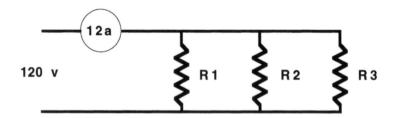

(a) 10   (b) 20   (c) 30   (d) 40

8. In the circuit shown below, the resistor that would use the most wattage would be the ____.

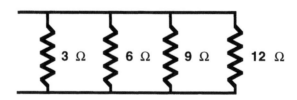

(a) 3Ω   (b) 6Ω   (c) 9Ω   (d) 12Ω

9. In the circuit shown below, if an additional resistor was connected in parallel to R2, the ammeter reading would ____.

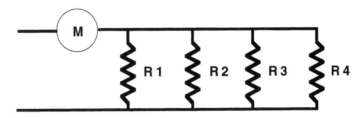

(a) read zero   (b) have no change   (c) increase in amperage   (d) decrease in amperage

10. In the circuit shown below, the source voltage would be ____ volts.

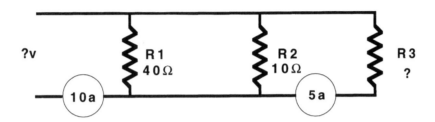

(a) 40   (b) 65   (c) 110   (d) 120

11. In the circuit shown above the resistance of R3 would be ____ ohms.

(a) 4   (b) 6   (c) 8   (d) 12

12. In the circuit shown below, if all three resistors are rated at 250 watts, which resistor or resistors would overheat?

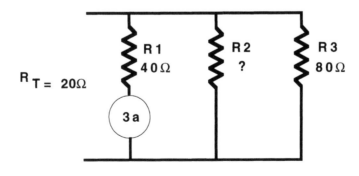

(a) R1   (b) R2   (c) R3   (d) none of them

13. The resistance of 40 feet of #18 AWG stranded and uncoated would be ____.

(a) 0.318 ohms   (b) 3.1 ohms   (c) 7.77 ohms   (d) 7.95 ohms

14. A 125 volt circuit has four 100 watt bulbs in series, the voltage drop across the third light would be ____ volts.

(a) 41.7   (b) 31.25   (c) 62.5   (d) 125

15. What would the ohmmeter read ?

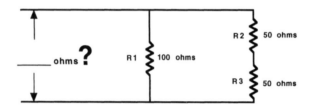

(a) 100 Ω   (b) 200 Ω   (c) 125Ω   (d) 50 Ω

16. The AC resistance of 1,000 feet of 500 kcmil uncoated copper conductor in a nonmetallic conduit is larger than the DC resistance of the same conductor in nonmetallic conduit by ____.

(a) 0.0258 ohms   (b) 0.036 ohms   (c) 0.0012 ohms   (d) 0.0102 ohms

17. A 1ø motor draws 23 amperes at 240 volts. If the circuit is 175 feet in length in conduit in free air, what is the minimum uncoated stranded Cu THW conductor size of the branch circuit recommended by the NEC?

(a) #10   (b) #8   (c) #12   (d) #4

18. What is the total resistance in the series-parallel circuit shown below?

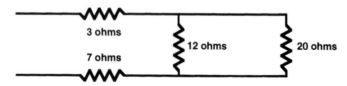

(a) 42Ω   (b) 4.28Ω   (c) 17.5Ω   (d) none of these

19. If the source of the branch circuit is 115 volts, the Code recommends a minimum of ___ volts at the load.

(a) 113.85   (b) 116.4   (c) 111.55   (d) 109.25

20. What is the total wattage of the circuit shown below?

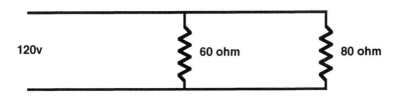

(a) 3.5   (b) 420   (c) 16,800   (d) 140

21. The circuit load is 140 amps. What is the voltage at the load?

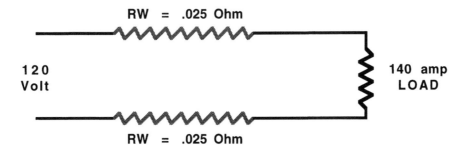

(a) 115 volts   (b) 113 volts   (c) 116.4 volts   (d) 120 volts

22. The resistance of a #12 THW solid aluminum conductor 160' long would be ____ Ω.

(a) 3.18   (b) .0508   (c) .52   (d) .5088

23. The minimum size conductor for a 1ø, 1 1/2hp, 10 amp motor, 150 feet from the source, would be a ____, if the voltage was 230 volts.

(a) #14 THW cu   (b) #12 THW cu   (c) #10 THW cu   (d) #8 THW cu

THE NEXT TWO QUESTIONS REFER TO THE DIAGRAM

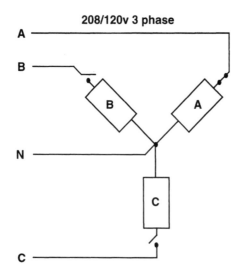

208/120v 3 phase

24. If load "A" is 9.6 kva and the voltage drop is not to exceed 3%, what size copper THW conductor is necessary if the load is located 90 feet from the source?

(a) #2   (b) #3   (c) #4   (d) none of these

25. What would load "A" be in amperes if located 60 feet from the source and fed by a #6 THW conductor and limited to 3% voltage drop?

(a) 104.04   (b) 100.04   (c) 60.02   (d) none of these

EXAM SPONSOR ______________________

DATE ______________________

TYPE EXAM ______________ PART ________

APPLICANT NUMBER								
0	0	0	0	0	0	0	0	0
1	1	1	1	1	1	1	1	1
2	2	2	2	2	2	2	2	2
3	3	3	3	3	3	3	3	3
4	4	4	4	4	4	4	4	4
5	5	5	5	5	5	5	5	5
6	6	6	6	6	6	6	6	6
7	7	7	7	7	7	7	7	7
8	8	8	8	8	8	8	8	8
9	9	9	9	9	9	9	9	9

GRADE ________

SAMPLE

THE NEUTRAL IS

A) red in color
B) black in color
C) blue in color
D) white in color

WRONG A B C D
WRONG A B C D
WRONG A B C D
WRONG A B C D
RIGHT A B C D

IMPORTANT DIRECTIONS FOR MARKING ANSWERS

- DO NOT USE INK OR BALLPOINT PEN
- USE BLACKLEAD #2 PENCIL ONLY
- MAKE HEAVY MARKS THAT FILL THE CIRCLE COMPLETELY
- ERASE CLEANLY ANY ANSWER YOU WISH TO CHANGE
- MAKE NO STRAY MARKS ON THE ANSWER SHEET

1 A B C D	21 A B C D	41 A B C D	61 A B C D	81 A B C D	101 A B C D
2 A B C D	22 A B C D	42 A B C D	62 A B C D	82 A B C D	102 A B C D
3 A B C D	23 A B C D	43 A B C D	63 A B C D	83 A B C D	103 A B C D
4 A B C D	24 A B C D	44 A B C D	64 A B C D	84 A B C D	104 A B C D
5 A B C D	25 A B C D	45 A B C D	65 A B C D	85 A B C D	105 A B C D
6 A B C D	26 A B C D	46 A B C D	66 A B C D	86 A B C D	106 A B C D
7 A B C D	27 A B C D	47 A B C D	67 A B C D	87 A B C D	107 A B C D
8 A B C D	28 A B C D	48 A B C D	68 A B C D	88 A B C D	108 A B C D
9 A B C D	29 A B C D	49 A B C D	69 A B C D	89 A B C D	109 A B C D
10 A B C D	30 A B C D	50 A B C D	70 A B C D	90 A B C D	110 A B C D
11 A B C D	31 A B C D	51 A B C D	71 A B C D	91 A B C D	111 A B C D
12 A B C D	32 A B C D	52 A B C D	72 A B C D	92 A B C D	112 A B C D
13 A B C D	33 A B C D	53 A B C D	73 A B C D	93 A B C D	113 A B C D
14 A B C D	34 A B C D	54 A B C D	74 A B C D	94 A B C D	114 A B C D
15 A B C D	35 A B C D	55 A B C D	75 A B C D	95 A B C D	115 A B C D
16 A B C D	36 A B C D	56 A B C D	76 A B C D	96 A B C D	116 A B C D
17 A B C D	37 A B C D	57 A B C D	77 A B C D	97 A B C D	117 A B C D
18 A B C D	38 A B C D	58 A B C D	78 A B C D	98 A B C D	118 A B C D
19 A B C D	39 A B C D	59 A B C D	79 A B C D	99 A B C D	119 A B C D
20 A B C D	40 A B C D	60 A B C D	80 A B C D	100 A B C D	120 A B C D

FINAL EXAM #2

1. A bank of lathes is operated by individual motors in a machine shop. The total current required to run the bank of lathes is 58 amperes at 240v, single phase. There is 250 feet of conduit between the main service panel and the sub-panel. The voltage drop in the feeder conductors may be a maximum of 3%. All terminations are listed for 75°C. Use resistance values for "uncoated" conductors in Chapter 9, Table 8 of the NEC. Each conductor in the feeder circuit to supply these lathes must be at least size _____ copper THW.

(a) #2 (b) #3 (c) #4 (d) #6

2. Given: A 2 kW load supplied by 240 volt single-phase with an 80% power factor. Each conductor has a net current of _____ amperes.

(a) 7.136 (b) 9.452 (c) 10.417 (d) 11.267

3. Given: A 10 ampere, 400 foot long resistance rated at 1.75 ohm/1000 feet. The voltage drop for 400 feet is _____ volts.

(a) 5 (b) 6 (c) 7 (d) 8

4. A resistor of 8 ohms and a resistor of 4 ohms are connected in series with a 12 volt power supply. The current through the 4 ohm resistor should measure _____ amperes.

(a) 0.5 (b) 0.67 (c) 1 (d) 1.5

5. A fire alarm horn is located 1500 feet from the control unit and requires a minimum applied voltage of 22.5 volts. The circuit supply voltage is 24 volts. At the minimum applied voltage the horn will draw 45 watts of power. The maximum total conductor resistance allowed for this installation is _____ ohms.

(a) .25 (b) .57 (c) .75 (d) 1.88

6. If a single-phase kiln rated at 53 amperes and 240 volts is operated on 208 volts, it will consume _____ power.

(a) 5.51 kW (b) 9.55 kW (c) 11.02 kW (d) 12.72 kw

7. A run of a 100 feet of #300 kcmil conductor has a voltage drop of 3%. If another length of #300 kcmil conductor is connected in parallel with the existing, the resulting voltage drop would be _____ percent.

(a) 1   (b) 1 1/2   (c) 2 1/2   (d) 3

8. Electricity cost $.085 per kW hour. The total cost to operate a 175 watt television for 10 continuous days is _____.

(a) $2.57   (b) $3.57   (c) $8.64   (d) $9.19

9. Copper at a temperature of 75°C has a resistance of 12.9Ω per circular-mil-foot. A solid copper conductor with a cross-sectional area of 10,380 cm has a resistance at 35°C of _____ Ω per thousand feet.

(a) 1.05   (b) 1.07   (c) 1.12   (d) 1.21

10. A 5 hp, 110 volt fan motor operating at 80% efficiency is replaced with the same sized motor operating at 90% efficiency. The new fan motor will draw _____ percent less current than the old fan.

(a) 11   (b) 20   (c) 25   (d) 30

11. The "Normal Current Density" of copper bus is 1,000 amperes per square inch. The number of amperes which a 2 1/2" x 1/4" copper bus bar may carry is _____ amperes.

(a) 500   (b) 625   (c) 1,000   (d) 1,250

12. Two distribution lines, Line A and Line B, each serve separate loads of 5000 kW. The load on Line A has a high power factor and the load on Line B has a low power factor. Which of the following statements about these two lines is true?

(a) Line A carries a higher current than Line B
(b) Line B carries a higher current than Line A
(c) Line A current is the same as Line B current
(d) Not enough information is given.

13. If a wire has a cross-sectional area of four (4) circulars mils, then the diameter of this wire is ____ inch.

(a) .002 (b) .004 (c) .020 (d) .040

14. A lighting load operating at 115 volts, 8 amperes, and a power factor of 80% will consume ____ watts of power.

(a) 736 (b) 920 (c) 1150 (d) 1273

15. A 460 volt branch circuit is allowed a maximum voltage drop of 4%. The minimum voltage at the branch circuit load is ____ volts.

(a) between 432.0 and 438.0   (b) between 438.1 and 440.0
(c) between 440.1 and 443.0   (d) between 443.1 and 446.0

16. Electricity costs $.085 per kilowatt hour. A 4.5 kW oven was left on maximum setting for approximately ____ hours. The cost of electricity was $5.00.

(a) 6 (b) 8 (c) 10 (d) 13

17. The largest available conductor for an electrical installation has a resistance of 1.5 ohms per 1,000 feet. To meet the voltage drop specifications, the maximum resistance of the circuit is 0.3 ohm. The maximum total length of conductor allowed in the circuit is ____ feet.

(a) 150 (b) 175 (c) 200 (d) 400

18. Refer to the diagram below. If the current through the circuit is 10 amperes, then the power factor is ____.

(a) .83 (b) .87 (c) .91 (d) 1.00

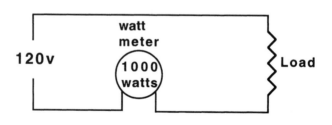

19. The wiring in a 200' long branch circuit measures a total resistance of 0.5 ohms. The resistance per 1000 feet would be _____ ohms.

(a) 1.5   (b) 2.0   (c) 2.5   (d) 4.5

20. A 240 volt, single-phase motor draws 10 amperes at a power factor of 0.9. The power output of the motor is _____ watts.

(a) 900   (b) 2,000   (c) 2,160   (d) 2,400

21. An electrical service transmission line decreases the initial voltage from 247 volts to 232 volts. The efficiency of the transmission line is approximately _____.

(a) 1.06%   (c) 90%   (c) 94%   (d) 100%

22. When charging a 12 volt battery with a 16 volt charger at an average amperage of 10 amperes, a _____ ohm resistor will be required in series with the charger.

(a) .4   (b) 1.2   (c) 1.6   (d) 4

23. If the allowable current density for copper bus bars is 1000 amperes per square inch, the current-carrying capacity of a circular copper bar having a diameter of 2" is approximately _____ amperes.

(a) 1050   (b) 2320   (c) 3140   (d) 4260

24. A 230 volt, single-phase circuit serves a 10 kilowatt load with 50 amperes of current. The power factor of the circuit is _____ per cent.

(a) 83   (b) 87   (c) 95   (d) 115

25. Refer to the diagram below. The combined total resistance is _____ ohms.

(a) 0.4   (b) 2.3   (c) 2.7   (d) 3.6

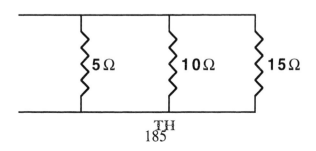

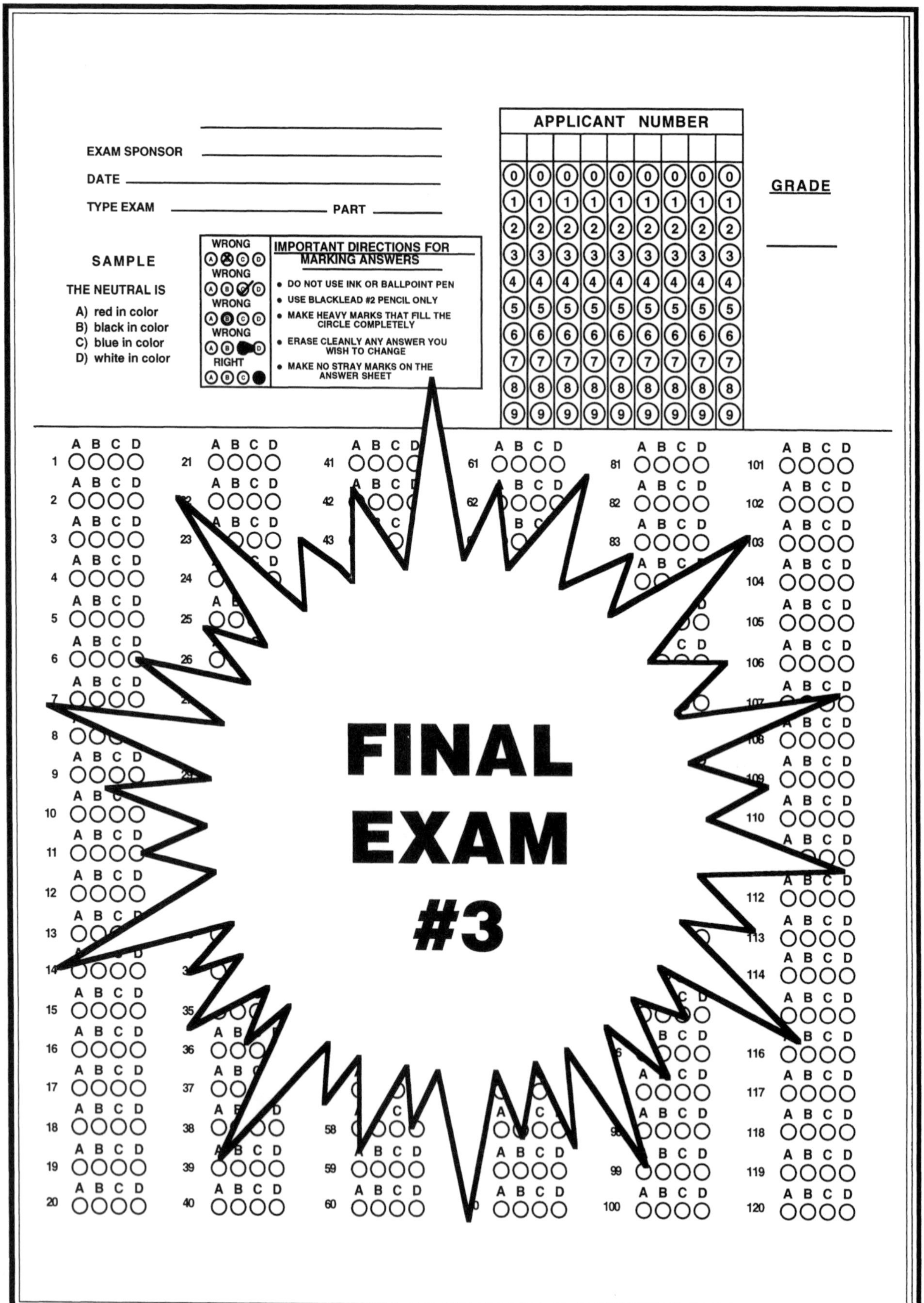

EXAM SPONSOR

DATE

TYPE EXAM _____ PART _____

APPLICANT NUMBER

GRADE

SAMPLE

THE NEUTRAL IS

A) red in color
B) black in color
C) blue in color
D) white in color

WRONG
WRONG
WRONG
WRONG
WRONG
RIGHT

IMPORTANT DIRECTIONS FOR MARKING ANSWERS

- DO NOT USE INK OR BALLPOINT PEN
- USE BLACKLEAD #2 PENCIL ONLY
- MAKE HEAVY MARKS THAT FILL THE CIRCLE COMPLETELY
- ERASE CLEANLY ANY ANSWER YOU WISH TO CHANGE
- MAKE NO STRAY MARKS ON THE ANSWER SHEET

FINAL EXAM #3

FINAL EXAM #3

1. The electric power cost is 8 cents per kwh. The cost to run a 5000 watt dryer for 8 hours is ____.

(a) $32.20   (b) $16.40   (c) $3.20   (d) $11.47

2. Refer to the diagram below. If the resistance across R4 is measured to be 10 ohms, the current through R4 is ____ amperes.

(a) 6   (b) 12   (c) 24   (d) 32

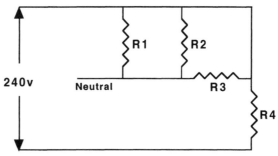

3. A 240v conductor has a total length of 500 feet, and supplies a load of 10 amperes. The conductor has a resistance of 1.45 ohms per 1,000 feet. The total voltage drop in the conductor circuit (wiring) is ____ percent.

(a) 2.5%   (b) 3%   (c) 3.5%   (d) 4%

4. Refer to the diagram below. If the current through R4 is measured to be 10 amperes, the electrical power consumption of R4 is ____ watts.

(a) 1,000   (b) 1,200   (c) 1,800   (d) 2,400

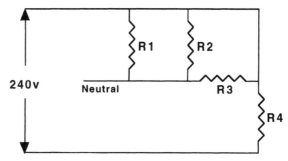

5. An electrical installation has a 115v load which consumes 1,000 watts. The voltage drop specification is 1%. The maximum total resistance of the wire in the circuit is _____ ohms.

(a) .07 (b) .09 (c) .13 (d) 2.3

6. Given only 21 ohm resistors, which of the following diagrams below would be used to achieve a total resistance of 14 ohms?

(a) A only (b) B only (c) A and C only (d) C and D only

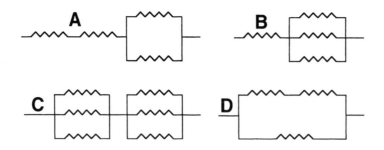

7. A 240v, single-phase circut has a load of 10 amps. The circuit has a combined length of 400 feet and a resistance of 1.75 ohms per 1000 feet. The total power lost in the conductor is _____ watts.

(a) 60 (b) 70 (c) 123 (d) 175

8. In the circuit shown below, the resistance at "X" is _____ ohms.

(a) 4.0 - 5.0 (b) 5.1 - 6.0 (c) 6.1 - 7.0 (d) 7.1 - 8.0

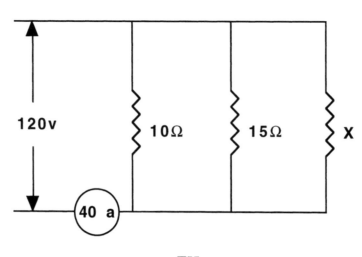

9. A 240v, 20 amp branch circuit, if the maximum allowable voltage drop through the wiring is 2.4 volts, the maximum allowable resistance of the wiring is _____ ohms.

(a) **122** (b) **12** (c) **1.2** (d) **.12**

10. Four electric heaters are installed and the resistance rating of each heater is 10 ohms, 20 ohms, 40 ohms and 50 ohms. If the heaters are wired in parallel, what is approximately the total resistance on a 240 volt circuit?

(a) **2 ohms** (b) **3 ohms** (c) **4.6 ohms** (d) **5 ohms**

11. Three heaters R1, R2, and R3 are installed in a series circuit. The power used by R1 is 100 watts and the power used by R2 is 75 watts. The power used by the circuit is 225 watts. The power used by heater R3 is _____ watts.

(a) **24** (b) **36** (c) **50** (d) **75**

12. Refer to the diagram below. The total resistance Rt is _____ ohms.

(a) **9.4** (b) **10.5** (c) **15** (d) **40**

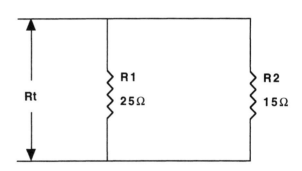

13. A 5 ohm resistor and a 10 ohm resistor are connected in parallel. If the common circuit feeding both resistors has a current of 15 amperes, the current through the 10 ohm resistor is _____ amperes.

(a) **5** (b) **8** (c) **10** (d) **15**

14. An electric range is rated 240 volts and draws 40 amps. The splice has .1 ohms resistance. How much power is being lost at the splice?

(a) .4 watts   (b) 40 watts   (c) 160 watts   (d) 400 watts

15. Refer to the diagram below. The voltage drop across A and B is 80 volts. The resistance values of R1, R2, R3 are equal. What is the total applied voltage?

(a) 80 volts   (b) 100 volts   (c) 120 volts   (d) 140 volts

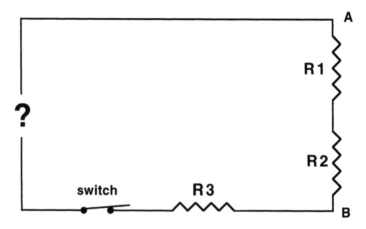

16. Refer to the diagram below. The total amperage through the 2 ohm resistor is _____ amperes.

(a) .4   (b) 1.0   (c) 2.8   (d) 4.0

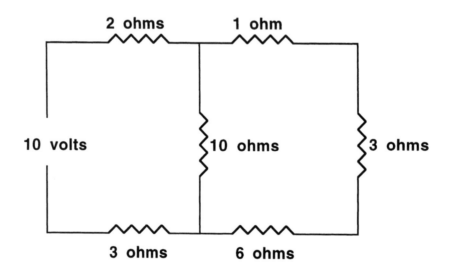

ANSWERS

EXAM 1 QUESTIONS

1. **(c)** magnetic field
2. **(c)** transformer
3. **(d)** 20 watts
4. **(c)** 70.7%
5. **(b)** all in parallel
6. **(b)** six
7. **(c)** cell

EXAM 2 QUESTIONS

1. **(a)** resistor
2. **(d)** Conductance
3. **(c)** ammeter
4. **(c)** automobile battery
5. **(c)** capacitive
6. **(c)** on multiwire circuits
7. **(b)** ease of voltage variation

EXAM 3 QUESTIONS

1. **(a)** copper & zinc
2. **(b)** power factor angle
3. **(d)** all liquids same density
4. **(b)** iron
5. **(c)** voltage drop
6. **(b)** AC generator larger than DC
7. **(d)** 1000va

EXAM 4 QUESTIONS

1. **(c)** current is common
2. **(c)** 3 ohms
3. **(b)** shorted
4. **(d)** relationship between E, I and R
5. **(d)** volts
6. **(c)** generator
7. **(b)** heat

EXAM 5 QUESTIONS

1. **(c)** change AC to DC
2. **(c)** farads
3. **(a)** ohms
4. **(d)** amp-hours
5. **(b)** voltage
6. **(c)** 2500
7. **(b)** piezoelectricity

EXAM 6 QUESTIONS

1. **(b)** parallel
2. **(a)** impedance
3. **(d)** henrys
4. **(a)** ohms
5. **(a)** DC rotating part is field
6. **(a)** voltage
7. **(b)** decrease

EXAM 7 QUESTIONS

1. **(a)** mica
2. **(c)** DC generator built larger than AC
3. **(d)** 1000
4. **(d)** any of these
5. **(b)** voltage difference
6. **(a)** revolving field AC generator
7. **(d)** 736w E x I x PF

EXAM 8 QUESTIONS

1. **(b)** AC only
2. **(b)** 746 watts
3. **(c)** 12 I = E/R
4. **(b)** cycles per second
5. **(c)** I = E/R
6. **(b)** 2.5 ohms
7. **(c)** 10 ohm resistor

EXAM 9   QUESTIONS

1. (c) good conductors
2. (b) 62.5 amp I = W/E
3. (c) paper
4. (a) material
5. (a) 30 Hz
6. (c) commutator
7. (c) DC

EXAM 10   QUESTIONS

1. (c) series-parallel
2. (b) revolution
3. (c) .001
4. (c) less than any one alone
5. (d) both I and II
6. (a) 30 hertz
7. (d) seldom

EXAM 11   QUESTIONS

1. (a) Ohm's law
2. (d) rectifiers change DC to AC is **false**
3. (c) water
4. (d) "ampacity" remains the same
5. (d) current
6. (c) resistance
7. (c) 90°

EXAM 12   QUESTIONS

1. (d) 75% 1800/20x120
2. (d) lower the resistance
3. (a) the ohm
4. (d) 1,000,000 ohms
5. (a) one amp
6. (b) pressure
7. (a) the sum of the individual resistance
       values

EXAM 13   QUESTIONS

1. (d) 1227w $R = E^2/W$ $W = E^2/R$
2. (d) DC for heavy torque
3. (c) capacitance
4. (c) 63.7%
5. (c) 17.5Ω
6. (a) reduce resistance by one-half

EXAM 14   QUESTIONS

1. (d) capacitive reactance exceeds
2. (c) ohms
3. (b) left
4. (c) balanced, nothing
5. (d) output
6. (c) electro

EXAM 15   QUESTIONS

1. (c) parallel
2. (b) increased-increase
3. (c) 6 volts series-parallel
4. (b) direct
5. (a) has many free electrons
6. (c) 9
7. (b) in a closed circuit

EXAM 16   QUESTIONS

1. (c) a power source
2. (c) II and III only
3. (a) 5 I=E/R 600v/120Ω
4. (a) I only
5. (c) 120v $E=\sqrt{WR}$
6. (d) resistance less than total in series

EXAM 17 QUESTIONS

1. **(a)** a loose connection
2. **(c)** 12 amps $I = \sqrt{W/R}$
3. **(b)** electrons passing a point per second
4. **(c)** watt hour
5. **(d)** series
6. **(c)** 1/120
7. **(a)** unity

EXAM 18 QUESTIONS

1. **(b)** equal to
2. **(d)** high conductance
3. **(c)** reduce it to its simplest form
4. **(c)** .6   450/746
5. **(d)** 6000 $W = I^2R$
6. **(c)** 220   W = E x I
7. **(b)** 420 I = E/R   W = E x I

EXAM 19 QUESTIONS

1. **(a)** current
2. **(d)** several thousand
3. **(b)** in parallel voltage is different
4. **(b)** high resistance will draw more current
5. **(a)** redraw the circuit
6. **(a)** 120

EXAM 20 QUESTIONS

1. **(c)** 70 amps
2. **(d)** each load lowers the resistance
3. **(d)** 1.0 unity
4. **(b)** start at the beginning
5. **(b)** resonance
6. **(d)** "X"

EXAM 21 QUESTIONS

1. **(a)** nonlinear
2. **(c)** the waveform is distorted
3. **(b)** AC through the csa
4. **(d)** 300 Hz
5. **(c)** neutral can be hotter

EXAM 22 SERIES-PARALLEL

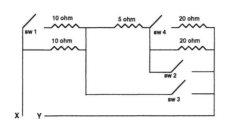

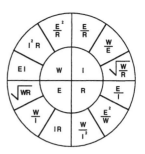

1. **(c)** 10Ω

10 ohm 5 ohm
10 ohm
$10Ω/2 = 5Ω$

= 5 ohm 5 ohm $5Ω + 5Ω = 10Ω$ total

2. **(a)** switches 1 and 3

10 ohm
10 ohm
$10Ω/2 = 5Ω$

3. **(d)** 105 volts

10 ohm 5 ohm 20 ohm $= 35Ω$ E = I x R $35Ω \times 3a = 105v$

4. **(a)** 500 watts

10 ohm
10 ohm
$10Ω/2 = 5Ω$

W = I2R

$10a \times 10a \times 5Ω = 500w$

5. **(b)** 90 volts

10 ohm 5 ohm 20 ohm
20 ohm
$20Ω/2 = 10Ω$

= 10 ohm 5 ohm 10 ohm

$10Ω + 5Ω + 10Ω = 25Ω$

I = E/R $225v/25Ω = 9a$

E = I x R $9a \times 10Ω = 90$ v

EXAM 23 QUESTIONS

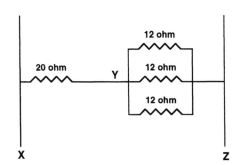

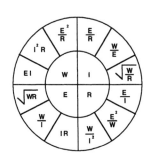

EACH OF THE 12Ω LOADS IS 2 AMPERES

1. **(b)** 864 watts

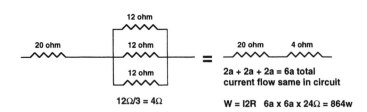

12Ω/3 = 4Ω

2a + 2a + 2a = 6a total
current flow same in circuit

W = I2R   6a x 6a x 24Ω = 864w

2. **(a)** 144 volts   E = I x R   6a x 24Ω = 144v

3. **(c)** 120 volts   E = I x R   6a x 20Ω = 120v

4. **(c)** 24 volts   E = I x R   6a x 4Ω = 24v or 144v - 120v = 24v

5. **(d)** 720 watts   W = I2R   6a x 6a x 20Ω = 720w

6. **(c)** 144w   W = I2R   6a x 6a x 4Ω = 144w

EXAM 24 QUESTIONS

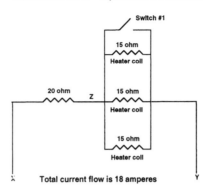

1. **(a)** 5 ohms

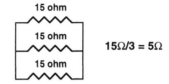

$15\Omega/3 = 5\Omega$

2. **(a)** 90 volts

E = I x R   18a x 5Ω = 90v

3. **(a)** 20 ohms

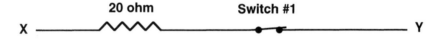

With sw #1 closed the three 15Ω loads are bypassed

4. **(c)** 450 volts

E = I x R   18a x 25Ω = 450v

EXAM 25 QUESTIONS

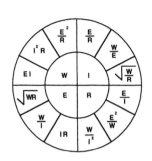

1. **(a)** 120 volts

I = E/R 48v/1200Ω = .04a   E = I x R .04a x 3000Ω = 120v

2. **(b)** 40 volts

I = E/R 120v/60Ω = 2a   E = I x R 2a x 20Ω = 40v

3. **(b)** 6 amps

I = E/R 120v/20Ω = 6a

4. **(c)** 4800 watts

12Ω/4 = 3Ω R total   W = E2/R 120v x 120v/3Ω = 4800w

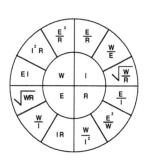

EXAM 26 QUESTIONS

1. **(c)** 19, 200 watts $12\Omega/4 = 3\Omega$ R total   W = E2/R   240v x 240v/3Ω = 19,200w

2. **(a)** 300 watts $12\Omega + 12\Omega + 12\Omega + 12\Omega = 48\Omega$ R total

    W = E2/R   120v x 120v/48Ω = 300w

3. **(c)** 120 watts   **R = E2/W   Resistance of one load 120v x 120v/120w = 120Ω**

    $120\Omega + 120\Omega + 120\Omega + 120\Omega = 480\Omega$ R total

    W = E2/R   240v x 240v/480Ω = 120w

4. **(b)** 36 volts   **E = I x R**

    I = E/R   120v/20Ω = 6a

    6a x 6Ω = 36v

ANSWERS

EXAM 27 QUESTIONS

1. **(b)** 240 watts **W = E2/R   120v x 120v/60Ω**

2. **(c)** 44 amps **I = E/R**

    240v/10Ω = 24a   240v/20Ω = 12a   240v/30Ω = 8a

    24a + 12a + 8a = 44a

3. **(a)** 3 amps **I = E/R   120v/40Ω = 3a**

4. **(c)** 8 ohms **I = E/R**

                        6Ω

10Ω   8Ω   =   10Ω   1.846Ω

        4Ω

10Ω + 1.846Ω = 11.846Ω R total

120v/11.846Ω = 10.13 amps current flow

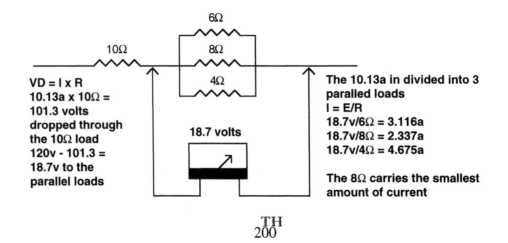

                    6Ω

       10Ω   8Ω

             4Ω

VD = I x R
10.13a x 10Ω =
101.3 volts
dropped through
the 10Ω load
120v - 101.3 =
18.7v to the
parallel loads

18.7 volts

The 10.13a in divided into 3
paralled loads
I = E/R
18.7v/6Ω = 3.116a
18.7v/8Ω = 2.337a
18.7v/4Ω = 4.675a

The 8Ω carries the smallest
amount of current

EXAM 28 QUESTIONS

1. (c) Higher
2. (d) EMF
3. (d) Volts
4. (a) It will double the previous reading
5. (b) 100 volts $E = I \times R$ $4a \times 25\Omega = 100v$

EXAM 29 QUESTIONS

1. (b) An ohmmeter requires its own power
2. (b) 1,600 watts $W = I^2R$ $20a \times 20a \times 4\Omega = 1600w$
3. (b) It will be the lowest at lagging power factors
4. (b) Instrument transformers
5. (d) A thermocouple
6. (d) 1,2,3, and 4. With switch 5 closed you have a 20Ω circuit.

EXAM 30 QUESTIONS

1. (a) 74.4 watts   •Current flows the same in series. $W = E \times I$ $120v \times .62a = 74.4w$
2. (d) EXCEPT significant resistance change
3. (d) $360°$ A complete cycle
4. (d) 1 watt $E \times I = W$
5. (d) EXCEPT a microwave oven
6. (c) multiplied by 4. $W = I^2R$
7. (d) ohms
8. (c) conductance

EXAM 31 QUESTIONS

1. (a) A proper size shunt is used
2. (b) voltage
3. (b) a larger inductance
4. (c) 20 ohms   smaller wire = higher resistance
5. (c) burning at full brilliance
6. (c) only a neutral carries unbalanced current

EXAM 32 QUESTIONS

1. (c) electrochemistry
2. (a) zero
3. (c) an insulator
4. (a) infinity
5. (c) 30Ω
6. (a) approximately zero
7. (c) open
8. (d) it makes the operation of each appliance independent with each other

EXAM 33 QUESTIONS

1. (c) inductive
2. (d) 600 amps $I = E/R$ $6v/.01\Omega = 600a$
3. (c) has voltage and current coils to measure real power
4. (b) 100 watts @240v Solution: Since the replacement bulb is connected across the same supply voltage, its resistance must be the same as the burnt out bulb, in order to draw the same amount of power. Resistance of burnt out bulb = E^2/W = 120v x 120v/25w = 576Ω

Choice (a) = 110v x 110v/20w = 605Ω
Choice (b) = 240v x 240v/100w = 576Ω
Choice (c) = 240v x 240v/50w = 1152Ω
Choice (d) = 220v x 220v/75w = 645Ω

5. (c) 6,000 watts   400v x 20a x .75PF = 6000w
6. (d) 660 watts   Solution: $1/Rt = 1/10 + 1/20 + 1/30$ lowest common demonminator is 60.
$$6/60 + 3/60 + 2/60 = 11/60 = Rt = 60/11 = 5.4545\Omega$$
$$W = E^2/R \qquad 60v \times 60v = 3600/5.4545 = 660 \text{ watts}$$

EXAM 34 QUESTIONS

1. (b) 6Ω Solution: $I=E/R$ 50v/10Ω= 5 amps current flow. Since in series the voltage across the resistor must be 30 volts and in order for the lamp to operate properly the current in a series circuit must be equal to 5 amps. $R = E/I$ = 30v/5a = 6 ohms.
2. (a) 19.2 watts $W = I^2R$ .8 x .8 x 30Ω = 19.2 watts
3. (d) none of these $E = I \times R$ 4a x 12Ω = 48v $I = E/R$ 48v/4Ω= 12a 48v/16Ω= 3a
       4a + 12a + 3a = 19 amp current flow
4. (c) open
5. (c) infinite
6. (a) zero
7. (b) watts
8. (d) all of these

EXAM 35 QUESTIONS

1. (a) peak to peak
2. (c) megohmmeter
3. (d) spark test
4. (d) thermocouple
5. (b) Measure the voltage across a known resistor.
6. (a) zero
7. (d) compensate aging battery of the meter
8. (b) infinity

VOLTAGE DROP EXAM 1

1. **(c) 5.6742 volts**.   Exact K = $\dfrac{1.93\Omega \times 6530cm}{1000'}$ = 12.6029

VD = $\dfrac{2 \times 12.6029 \times 150' \times 9.8a}{6530\ cm}$ = 5.6742 volts dropped

(or) VD = I x R   9.8a x .579Ω (1.93 x .300') = 5.6742 volts dropped

2. **(b) 2.9953 volts**. Exact K = $\dfrac{.778\Omega \times 16510cm}{1000'}$ = 12.84478

VD = $\dfrac{2 \times 12.84478 \times 175' \times 11a}{16510\ cm}$ = 2.9953 volts dropped

3. **(c) #10**. CM = $\dfrac{1.732 \times 12.9 \times 180' \times 15a}{6.24v\ (3\%\ of\ 208v)}$ = 9667.5cm required   Table 8 = #10 @ 10380cm

4. **(b) 181.45 feet**. Exact K = $\dfrac{1.24\Omega \times 10380cm}{1000'}$ = 12.8712

D = $\dfrac{10380cm \times 7.2v}{2 \times 12.8712 \times 16a}$ = 181.45 feet distance

5. **(d) 5.80 amps**. Exact K = $\dfrac{1.98\Omega \times 6530cm}{1000'}$ = 12.9294

I = $\dfrac{6530cm \times 3.45v}{2 \times 12.9294 \times 150'}$ = 5.80 amps

6. **(b) #12 THW cu**. CM = $\dfrac{2 \times 12.9 \times 150' \times 10a}{6.9\ VD\ permitted}$ = 5608cm required   Table 8 = #12 @ 6530cm

7. **(d) 4.851 volts**. Exact K = $\dfrac{1.26\Omega \times 16510cm}{1000'}$ = 20.8026

VD = $\dfrac{2 \times 20.8026 \times 175' \times 11a}{16510cm}$ = 4.851 volts

VOLTAGE DROP EXAM 2

1. **(a) 115 volts.** R total = .025Ω + .025Ω = .05Ω Rt   VD = I x R = 100a x .05Ω = 5 volts dropped
   120 volt source - 5 volts dropped = 115 volts at the load

2. **(b) #3.** Use approximate K for aluminum 21.2
   CM = $\dfrac{2 \times 21.2 \times 148' \times 60a}{7.2 \text{ VD permitted}}$ = 52,293cm required   Table 8 = #3 @ 52,620cm

3. **(b) 150-160 feet.** Exact K = $\dfrac{1.93Ω \times 6530cm}{1000'}$ = 12.6029

   D = $\dfrac{6530cm \times 12v}{2 \times 12.6029 \times 20a}$ = 155.44 feet distance

   •Note: In a short circuit, **all** of the source voltage is dropped.

4. **(b) 115 volts.** Current flows the same in a series circuit: I = E/R   5v/1Ω = 5 amps flowing
   E = I x R   5a x 20Ω = 100 volts
   5a x 2Ω = 10 volts
   5a x 1Ω =   5 volts
   $\overline{ 115 \text{ volts}}$

5. **(b) 114 volts.** Total VD permitted = 120v x 5% = 6 volts total.
   120v - 116.5 = 3.5v dropped in the feeder
   6v total - 3.5v dropped = 2.5v left to drop in the branch circuit
   116.5v - 2.5v = 114 volts at the load

VOLTAGE DROP EXAM 3

1. **(a) 102 feet**. Table 8: #6 = $.491\Omega$ per k/ft = $.000491\Omega$ per foot.
                              $\overline{1000'}$

$\dfrac{.05\Omega \text{ total R}}{.000491\Omega \text{ per foot}}$ = 101.8 feet of conductor

2. **(b) 0.074**. #4 THW cu for 54a x 125%(430.22) = 67.5 required ampacity for a motor
          Exact K = $\dfrac{.308\Omega \text{ x } 41740cm}{1000'}$ = 12.85592

          D = $\dfrac{41740cm \text{ x } 6.9vd}{1.732 \text{ x } 12.85592 \text{ x } 54a}$ = 239.5 feet

          #4 = $.308\Omega$ per k/ft x .2395' = 0.073766Ω or .074

3. **(c) 61 feet**. Exact K = $\dfrac{.491\Omega \text{ x } 26240cm}{1000'}$ = 12.88384

          D = $\dfrac{26240cm \text{ x } 3.6 \text{ VD}}{2 \text{ x } 12.88384 \text{ x } 60a}$ = 61 feet distance

4. **(a) .0173145 ohm**. Table 8: #2 copper = $.194\Omega$ x .085" = $.01649\Omega$

          For 90°C increase $.01649\Omega$ x 1.05 = $.0173145\Omega$

5. **(b) #10**. Use approximate K 12.9 for copper

          CM = $\dfrac{1.732 \text{ x } 12.9 \text{ x } 126' \text{ x } 15a}{6.24 \text{ VD}}$ = 6767.2cm required Table 8: #10 @ 10380cm

6. **(d) 76-90 feet**. Exact K = $\dfrac{.808\Omega \text{ x } 26240cm}{1000'}$ = 21.20192

          D = $\dfrac{26240cm \text{ x } 3.6 \text{ VD}}{2 \text{ x } 21.20192 \text{ x } 50a}$ = 44.55' distance

          44.55' distance x 2 (single-phase) = 89.1' length of conductor

VOLTAGE DROP EXAM 4

1. **(b) .053 ohm**.   Table 8: #2 aluminum = .319Ω per k/ft x .167' = .053Ω

2. **(d) 259.9 feet**.   Exact K = $\dfrac{.308Ω \text{ x } 41740cm}{1000'}$ = 12.85592

$$D = \dfrac{41740cm \text{ x } 6.24 \text{ VD}}{1.732 \text{ x } 12.85592 \text{ x } 45a} = 259.9 \text{ feet distance}$$

3. **(c) .0032 ohm**.   Table 8: #500 kcmil = .0258Ω per k/ft x .250' = .00645Ω

$\dfrac{.00645Ω}{2}$ = .0032Ω   Equal resistance in parallel = $\dfrac{\text{resistance of one}}{\text{number of resistances}}$

4. **(c) 19.2 amps**.   Exact K = $\dfrac{1.24Ω \text{ x } 10380cm}{1000'}$ = 12.8712

$$I = \dfrac{10380cm \text{ x } 6.6 \text{ VD}}{1.732 \text{ x } 12.8712 \text{ x } 160'} = 19.2 \text{ amps maximum load permitted}$$

5. **(c) 105.5 volts**.   Table 8: #8 stranded coated = .809 Ω per k/ft x .150' = .12135Ω
#6 aluminum   = .808 Ω per k/ft x .150' = .1212 Ω
.24255Ω total

VD = I x R   60 amps x .24255Ω = 14.553 volts dropped

Source voltage 120 - 14.5vd = 105.5v

VOLTAGE DROP EXAM 5

1. **(a) 41 feet**. Table 8: #6 THW = .491Ω per k/ft = .000491Ω per foot

$$\frac{.04\Omega \text{ total R}}{.000491\Omega \text{ per ft}} = \frac{81.4' \text{ of conductor}}{2 \text{ conductors}} = 40.7' \text{ distance}$$

2. **(a) #1**. First step: Find the voltage drop in the 150' of copper to find out how many volts are left to drop in the 150' of aluminum without exceeding the recommended 3% total.

VD = I x R   Table 8: #4 = .308Ω per k/ft x .300' = .0924Ω

VD = 40a x .0924Ω = 3.696 volts dropped in 150' of copper conductor

VD permitted 3% of 240v = 7.2v   7.2v - 3.696v = 3.504v left to drop

$$CM = \frac{2 \times 21.2 \times 150' \times 40a}{3.504 \text{ volts left}} = 72,602.7 \text{cm required}$$ Table 8: #1 @ 83,690cm

3. **(b) 5.73 amps**. Exact $K = \dfrac{3.14\Omega \times 4110\text{cm}}{1000'} = 12.9054$

$$I = \frac{4110\text{cm} \times 3.6 \text{ VD}}{2 \times 12.9054 \times 100'} = 5.73 \text{ amps maximum load permitted}$$

4. **(c) 4.928 volts**. Exact $K = \dfrac{1.28\Omega \times 16510\text{cm}}{1000'} = 21.1328$

$$VD = \frac{2 \times 21.1328 \times 175' \times 11a}{16510\text{cm}} = 4.928 \text{ volts dropped}$$

5. **(c) 181 feet**. Exact $K = \dfrac{1.24\Omega \times 10380\text{cm}}{1000'} = 12.8712$

$$D = \frac{10380\text{cm} \times 7.2 \text{ VD}}{2 \times 12.8712 \times 16a} = 181 \text{ feet distance}$$

6. **(b) 0.39 ohm**. Table 9: #8 copper in steel conduit = 0.78Ω x .500' = 0.39Ω

VOLTAGE DROP EXAM 6

1. I. **(b) #8**. The **total** voltage drop permitted is 5% of 240v = 12 volts. First step: Find the voltage
drop in the branch circuit to determine how many volts are left to drop in the feeder.
VD = I x R   Table 8: #6 THW alum. = .808Ω per k/ft x .260' = .21008Ω
Branch circuit VD = 24a x .21008Ω = 5.04192 volts dropped in the branch circuit
Total permitted VD = 12v - 5.04192v = 6.95808v left to drop in the feeder
CM = $\frac{2 \times 12.9 \times 180' \times 24a}{6.95808v \text{ left}}$ = 16,018cm required   Table 8 = #8 @ 16,510cm

II. **(c) 11.76 volts**. The branch circuit has 5.04192 voltage drop. Find the actual voltage drop in the
feeder using the #8 conductor selected.
VD = I x R   Table 8: #8 = .778Ω x .360' = .28008Ω
VD = 24a x .28008Ω = 6.72192 volts dropped in the feeder
Feeder actual VD   = 6.72192v
Branch circuit actual VD = 5.04192v
                                     11.76384 total voltage drop, within the 5% 12 volt

2. **(d) 228 volt**.   240v x 5% = 12 VD permitted   240v - 12v = 228 volts

3. **(c) #3 THW**.   CM = $\frac{2 \times 12.9 \times 350' \times 40a}{6.9 \text{ VD}}$ = 52,347 cm required   Table 8: #3 @ 52,620cm

4. **(c) #1 THW**.   6000w/120v = 50 amp load

CM = $\frac{2 \times 12.9 \times 200' \times 50a}{3.6 \text{ VD}}$ = 71,666cm required   Table 8: #1 @ 83,690cm

VOLTAGE DROP EXAM 7

1. **(d) 7.2 volts**.   240v x 3% = 7.2v

2. **(a) 2.6%**.   3v/115v = 2.6%

3. **(d) #6 THW**.   CM = $\dfrac{2 \times 12.9 \times 225' \times 12a}{3.6 \text{ VD}}$ = 19,350cm required   Table8: #6 @ 26240cm

4. **(d) none of these**. A 45 amp load would require a #8 THW copper with an ampacity of 50.

$$\text{Exact K} = \frac{.764\Omega \times 16510cm}{1000'} = 12.61364$$

$$D = \frac{16510cm \times 3 \text{ volts (actual drop 115-112)}}{2 \times 12.61364 \times 45a} = 43.6 \text{ feet distance}$$

5. **(d) none of these**. $\dfrac{360,000va}{208v \times 1.732}$ = 999 amp load

$$CM = \frac{1.732 \times 12.9 \times 200' \times 999a}{6.24 \text{ VD}} = 715,399cm \text{ required}$$

   •Note: Always check to see if the conductor has the ampacity to carry the
   load from Table 310.16. A #750 kcmil **won't** carry 999 amps!

6. **(c) .0012 ohm**.   Table 9 = .027Ω   Table 8 = .0258Ω   difference of .0012Ω

7. **(a) 0.14475 ohm**.   Table 8: #12 solid = 1.93Ω per k/ft x .150' = .2895Ω

$$\text{Parallel} = \frac{.2895\Omega}{2 \text{ conductors}} = .14475\Omega$$

VOLTAGE DROP EXAM 8

1. **(c) 6.336 volts** VD = I x R Table 8 #12 stranded 1.98Ω x .200' = .396Ω x 16a F.L.C. = 6.336 VD

2. **(b) 36 feet** Table 8 #6 = .491Ω per k ft./1000' = .000491 Ω per foot .035Ω/.000491Ω = 71.28'
Length of **ONE** conductor would be 71.28'/2 = 35.6 or 36 feet

3. **(b) 116 feet**   D = 83690cm x 3.6 vd / 2 x 12.88826 x 100a = 116.8'

4. **(b) 3.58 volts**   VD = 2 x 12.88826 x 116' x 100a / 83690cm = 3.572 volts

5. **(a) 9.43%**   530v - 480v = 50 volts dropped. 50v/530v = 9.43%

VOLTAGE DROP EXAM 9

1. **(d) 400 kcmil**   On large loads with a distance always compare ampacity with voltage drop.
VD = 1.732 x 12.9 x 100' x 333a/ 6.24 vd permitted = 119,233 cm required = #2/0. **But,**
Table 310.16 requires a 400 kcmil THW to carry 333 amperes

2. **(c) 91.8 feet**   VD permitted = 120v x 3% = 3.6v   Load = 9600va/120v = 80a
Distance = 52620cm x 3.6vd / 2 x 12.8919 x 80a = 91.8 feet

3. **(b) #10**

118 v   **sub panel**   **#6 THW**   **60'**   **150'**   **11.5a motor**

VD = I x R   #6 = .491Ω x .120' = .05892Ω x 11.5a = .67758 VD
Permitted VD = 118v x 5% = 5.9 volts.   5.9v - .67758v = 5.22242 volts left to drop
CM = 2 x 12.9 x 150' x 11.5a / 5.22242vd = 8521.9 or 8522cm required   Table 8 = #10 wire

4. **(b) 1.25Ω**   R=E/I = 20vd/16a = 1.25Ω

FINAL EXAM #1

1. **(c) 10Ω**   40 x 10 = $\dfrac{400}{50}$ = 8Ω rt
                 40 + 10 =

2. **(d) highest through the 3Ω resistor** (low resistance - high current)

3. **(a) 2 amps**   I=E/R = 120v/60Ω = 2a

4. **(b) 6 amps**   current adds in parallel 120v/120Ω = 1a   120v/60Ω = 2a 120v/40Ω = 3a

5. **(d) 240 volts**   E = I x R   18a-10a = 8a in R2   8a x 30Ω = 240v

6. **(a) 24 ohms**   E = I x R   10a x 24Ω = 240v

7. **(c) 30 ohms**   R = E/I   120v/12a = 10Ω $\dfrac{30\Omega \text{ resistance of one}}{3 \text{ number of resistors}}$ = 10Ω

8. **(a) 3Ω**   W = I²R   lowest R = highest I which is squared

9. **(c) increase in amperage**   as you have another load

10. **(a) 40 volts**   you have to use one of the answer choices, it's better to answer #11 first!

11. **(c) 8 ohms**   By selecting 40v a *choice* of answer E = I x R = 5a x 8Ω = 40v

12. **(a) R1**   E = I x R = 3a x 40Ω = 120v W = I²R   R1 = 3a x 3a x 40Ω = 360w
               I = E/R = 120v/80Ω = 1.5a   R3 = 1.5a x 1.5a x 80Ω = 180w
               R2 is also 80Ω and 180w

13 . **(a) 0.318 ohms**   Table 8 = 7.95Ω per k/ft x .040' = .318Ω

14. **(b) 31.25 volts**   current flows the same in series   125v/4 bulbs = 31.25 drop at each

15. **(d) 50Ω**   R1 + R2 50Ω + 50Ω = 100Ω in parallel with 100Ω = 100Ω/2 = 50Ω

16. **(c) 0.0012 ohms**   Table 9 =   .027Ω
                         Table 8 = - .0258Ω
                                   ‾‾‾‾‾‾‾
                                     .0012

17. **(b) #8** $CM = \dfrac{2 \times 12.9 \times 175' \times 23a}{7.2 \text{ vd}}$ = 14,423 cm required   Table 8 = #8

18. **(c) 17.5Ω** $\dfrac{12\Omega \times 20\Omega = 240}{12\Omega + 20\Omega = \ 32} = 7.5\Omega + 3\Omega + 7\Omega = 17.5\Omega$

19. **(c) 111.55 volts**   115v x 3% = 3.45vd permitted   115v - 3.45v = 111.55v

20. **(b) 420 watts**   first find I = E/R   120v/60Ω = 2a   120v/80Ω = 1.5a   2a + 1.5a = 3.5a
    W = E x I   120v x 3.5a = 420 watts

21. **(b) 113 volts**   VD = I x R   Find Rt = .025Ω + .025Ω = .05Ω Rt   140a x .05Ω = 7v
    120v - 7v = 113v

22. **(d) .5088Ω**   Table 8 = 3.18Ω per k/ft x .160' = .5088Ω

23. **(b) #12** $CM = \dfrac{2 \times 12.9 \times 150' \times 10a}{6.9\text{vd}}$ = 5608 cm required   Table 8 = #12

24. **(b) #3**   first find I = va/E = 9600va/120v = 80 amps

    $CM = \dfrac{2 \times 12.9 \times 90' \times 80a}{3.6\text{vd}}$ = 51,600 cm required Table 8 = #3

25. **(d) none of these**   first find exact K = $\dfrac{.491\Omega \times 26240cm}{1000'}$ = 12.88384

    I = $\dfrac{26240cm \times 3.6 \text{ vd}}{2 \times 12.88384 \times 60'}$ = 61.099 or 61.1 amps

FINAL EXAM #2

1. **(b) #3**   Wire Size: CM = 2 x K x D x I/ VD permitted (3% x 240v =7.2v)
              2 x 12.9 x 250' x 58a/ 7.2vd = 51,958 cm required
    Table 8: = #3 has 52,620 cm

2. **(c) 10.417 amperes**   I = W/E x PF   2000w/240v x .8 PF = 10.4166 amperes

3. **(c) 7 volts** R = 1.75Ω/1000' = .00175Ω per ft. x 400' = .7 ohms
    VD = I x R 10a x .7Ω = 7 volts

4. **(c) 1**   Total series resistance is 8Ω + 4Ω = 12Ω   I = 12v/12Ω = 1 amp current flow is
    the same through both resistors in a SERIES circuit.

5. **(c) .75 ohms**   Find the current   I = W/E   45w/22.5v = 2 amps
    R = E/I   E = 24v - 22.5v = 1.5v   1.5v/2a = .75 ohms

6. **(b) 9.55 kW**   Find R   240v/53a = 4.53 ohms fixed resistance
    W = E²/R   208v x 208v/4.53Ω = 9550 watts/1000 = 9.55 kW

7. **(b) 1 1/2%**   By paralleling equal resistances you cut the resistance in half, thus you
    reduce the voltage drop by one half from 3% to 1 1/2%.

8. **(b) $3.57**   Cost = Rate x kW x Hours $.085 x .175 kW x 240 hrs. = $3.57

9. **(b) 1.07Ω**   Table 8 Footnotes #2: 75°C - 35°C = 40°C x .00323 coefficient for copper =
    .1292 + 1 = 1.1292 factor. Table resistance for a #10 solid copper conductor
    is 1.21Ω per thousand feet @ 75°C. 1.21Ω/1.1292 factor = 1.07Ω for a
    thousand feet of #10 solid copper @ 35°C.

10. **(a) 11%**   I = W/E   5hp x 746w = 3730w/110vx.80 = 42.38a
    3730w/110vx.90 = 37.67a
    42.38a - 37.67a = 4.71a   4.71a/42.38a = .11 x 100 = 11% less current

11. **(b) 625 amperes**   2.5" x .25" = .625 sq.in. x 1000a = 625 amperes

12. **(b) Line B carries a higher current than Line A**
    The line with a low power factor will have a higher current.

13. **(a) .002 inch**   √4 = 2/1000 = .002

14. **(a) 736 watts**   W = E x I x PF   115v x 8a x 80% = 736 watts

15. **(c) betwen 440.1 and 443.0**   460v x 4% = 18.4 vd   460v - 18.4 vd = 441.6v at the
    load (or) 460v x 96% = 441.6v

FINAL EXAM #2

16. **(d) 13 hours**   Hours = Cost/rate/kw = \$5/.085/4.5kW = 13.07 hours

17. **(c) 200 feet**   1.5Ω/1000' = .0015Ω per foot   .3Ω/.0015Ω = 200 feet

18. **(a) .83 PF**   PF = W/VA   1000w/1200va = .83

19. **(c) 2.5 ohms**   1000'/200' = 5 x .5Ω = 2.5Ω per 1000'

20. **(c) 2,160 watts**   W = PF x VA   240v x 10a = 2400va x .9 = 2160w

21. **(c) 94%**   232v/247v = 93.9 or 94%

22. **(a) .4 ohm**   R = E/I   R = 12v/10a = 1.2Ω   Using a 16v charger
                                     R = 16v/10a = 1.6Ω
                                       Need to add a resistance of 1.6Ω - 1.2Ω = .4 ohms added

23. **(c) 3140 amperes**   2" x 2" = 4 sq.in. x 1000a = 4000a x .7854 (convert sq.in. to circular)
                                    = 3142 amps

24. **(b) 87%**   VA = E x I   230v x 50a = 11,500va
                 10,000w/11,500va = .869 or 87%

25. **(c) 2.7 ohms** $\dfrac{5Ω \times 10Ω = 50}{5Ω + 10Ω = 15}$ = 3.33Ω $\dfrac{3.33Ω \times 15Ω = 49.95}{3.33Ω + 15Ω = 18.33}$ = 2.72Ω total R

FINAL EXAM #3

1. **(c) $3.20**   Cost = .08 kwh x 5 kw x 8 hours = $3.20

2. **(c) 24 amperes**   I = E/R $240v/10\Omega = 24$ amps

3. **(b) 3%**   VD = I x R   R = $1.45\Omega/2 = .725\Omega$ for 500' of wire
10a x .725Ω = 7.25VD   7.25v/240v = .0302 or 3%

4. **(d) 2,400 watts**   W = E x I   240v x 10a = 2400 watt

5. **(c) .13 ohms**   R = E/I   I = W/E   1,000w/115v = 8.7 amps
VD = 115v x 1% = 1.15v   R = 1.15v/8.7a = .13Ω

6. **(d) C and D only** You can eliminate A & B circuits since the series resistance will be 21Ω or
greater.   C = R of one =21Ω/3 = 7Ω + 7Ω = 14Ω
D = 21Ω + 21Ω = 42Ω and 21Ω
$$\frac{42\Omega \times 21\Omega = 882}{42\Omega + 21\Omega = \ 63} = 14\Omega$$

7. **(b) 70 watts**   Power loss = I^2R R = 1.75Ω/1000' = .00175Ω per ft. x 400' = .7Ω
10a x 10a x .7Ω = 70 watts

8. **(b) 5.1 - 6.0 ohms** Find R total: R = E/I 120v/40a = 3Ω Rt   Find resistance of the two.
$$\frac{10\Omega \times 15\Omega = 150}{10\Omega + 15\Omega = \ 25} = 6\Omega \qquad \frac{R \ of \ one \qquad = 6\Omega}{Number \ of \ R \ \ = 2} = 3\Omega \ total \ R \quad X = 6\Omega$$

9. **(d) .12 ohms**   R = E/I 2.4 VD/20a = .12Ω

10. **(d) 5 ohms** $\frac{10\Omega \times 20\Omega = 200}{10\Omega + 20\Omega = \ 30}$ 200/30 = 6.66 $\frac{6.66 \times 40 = 266.4}{6.66 + 40 = 46.66}$ 266.4/46.7 = 5.7
$\frac{5.7 \times 50\Omega \ = 285}{5.7 + 50\Omega \ = \ 55.7}$ 285/55.7 = 5.11 R total

11. **(c) 50 watts**   225w - 100w = 125w 125w - 75w = 50 watt for R3

12. **(a) 9.4 ohms**   25Ω x 15Ω = 375
25Ω + 15Ω = 40   375/40 = 9.375Ω R total

FINAL EXAM #3

13. **(a) 5 amperes**   Find R total: $\dfrac{5\Omega \times 10\Omega = 50}{5\Omega + 10\Omega = 15}$ $50/15 = 3.33\Omega$ Rt
Find E: E = I x R 15a x 3.33Ω = 50 volts
I = 50v/10Ω = 5 amperes

14. **(c) 160 watts**   VD = I x R   40a x .1Ω = 4 volts   W = E x I   4v x 40a = 160 watts

15. **(c) 120 volts**   Series circuit. The resistors are equal value.
80 volts dropped/2 resistors = 40 VD per resistor.
40v x 3 resistors = 120v applied.

16. **(b) 1.0 amperes**   Start at the end of circuit, 1Ω, 3Ω, 6Ω are in series combined them into one
10Ω which now is in paralled with the other 10Ω. Formula for equal
parallel: Resistance of one/Number of resistors = 10Ω/2 resistors = 5Ω.
Now the circuit has a 2Ω,5Ω,3Ω = series for total R of 10Ω.
I = E/R   10v/10Ω = 1 amp total current flow.

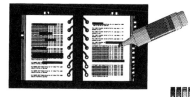

 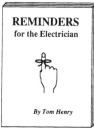